UND
&OVE...

**UEA UNDERGRADUATE
ANTHOLOGY 2020-2021**

So here we are, the fifth year that Egg Box, UEA's publishing society, have had the honour of producing UEA's Creative Writing Undergraduate Anthology—and what a year! This time a year ago, we were amid copyediting UEA's previous Undergraduate anthology, Underscore, when it was announced that the UK would be heading into lockdown. Now, we find ourselves experiencing the longitudinal effects of the pandemic, the social restrictions of lockdown threatening the thriving community within UEA's Creative Writing course. Despite this, UEA's Creative Writing students have continued to produce an excellent standard of work, evident in the contents of this anthology, and the effort that our members here at Egg Box have invested into its editing and marketing. The cultural context in which we published this anthology is like no other, and it's for this reason we chose the title Under & Over, to recognise the troughs from which many of our writers have had to pull themselves from during this pandemic, and the peaks they have climbed in doing so. It is with this in mind that we thank the students who have contributed to this anthology, their enthusiasm and support being the fuel behind its publication.

The Egg Box Publishing Society offers its members a wide range of opportunities under the umbrella of publishing, including working on the shortlisting team for Boiler House Press, producing and contributing to our variety of zines, and of course, editing and marketing for the Undergraduate Creative Writing Anthology. This year we mourned the absence of open mics, literary festivals, and other opportunities for performance and the celebration of creativity. However, this loss encouraged our committee members to nurture a communicative space for Norwich's writers, not just through the publication of Under & Over, but through online mentorship schemes and creative writing workshops. Although the new norm is to flinch at the approach of a stranger on Norwich's cobblestones, and wind our paths to six feet apart, the quality of contributions to this anthology shows that UNESCO's City of Literature is still thriving in terms of its creative community. At the back of this book, you will see the names of those who worked on this anthology, in recognition of their contribution.

Producing the anthology completely online, with no in-person communication, has exemplified the perseverance of UEA's Creative Writing students as they worked from all around the globe to present the proudest writing of our peers. A huge thanks goes to Nathan Hamilton and Philip Langeskov, and the school of Literature, Drama and Creative Writing, who have provided opportunities and support to our members in the rewarding sphere of publishing through these unstable circumstances. Reading the work of our peers and seeing their continued engagement with the anthology reaffirmed our own value of the arts as a sphere of catharsis and escape. We hope you enjoy the work of our peers in this anthology, and it offers you some relief also.

All the best,
The Egg Box Editing Team

BART, BRING MILK

Tom Rosser

Bart holds the steering wheel with his knees, pulls the lid off his thermos and pours coffee. Ovals of ice warp the view through the windscreen like pockets of air trapped in an adhesive plastic film. In the distance, fields break out into pockmarks of little wooden sheds and streaks of white fencing. Something goes under the right tyre—two bumps: one front, one back. He drops the lid, scalds himself, steers against the skid. Rubber on frost. Fingernails over velvet. The run of brittle mud between the tarmac and the ditch restores traction and the car rocks to a stop.

Hot panic and coffee fill Bart's nostrils like fat fingers. Foot off the brake, handbrake up; mysterious under-workings creak. Hazard lights on; tick, tock, tick, tock. The engine cools, tip, tip…tip tap. He blinks the stinging out of his eyes then lets it all out.

Something jumps out of the AC vent and claws into the hot flesh behind Bart's ear. A flea.

'How dreadfully unfair,' mutters the flea to itself, deftly reaching with all its needles through the panel of skin to the flowing red stream beneath, '…terribly unfair.'

Bart, unaware of the new resident on his neck, mutters aloud to himself, 'What did I hit?'

'You hit a fox,' replies the flea, knowing it can't be heard. It speaks around a mouthful, noting the quality of the new flavour. 'But don't feel too bad. It was finished, anyway.'

Bart gets out of the car and finds the weather is such that he can look at the sun without squinting. A perfect circle, radiance diffused in thick vapour. He stoops at the front of his car and finds no damage, only a moist, red spray across the tyre. The fox lies dead nearby.

'Nasty business. The tyre got him in the neck, spun him like flax, made a bow-string out of him…' The flea pauses to wipe its mouth on a handkerchief, 'You'd better bury him.'

'I'd better move him,' Bart unwittingly concurs, and uses his foot to nudge the empty body off the tarmac, into the ditch. It seems to bleed remarkably little. 'Rest in peace.'

'My compliments to the chef,' says the flea with a bloody grin.

Bart's fingers flutter for the, handle of the driver-side door but it doesn't open when he pulls.

'Have you locked yourself out?' enquires the flea, huddling close to the heated panel of flesh, mandibles chattering from cold.

Bart gives the window three quick, sharp knocks with his knuckle. After a short pause, it opens just a crack and a voice from inside the car says, 'Yes?'

'Excuse me, but that's my seat,' says Bart.

A pause hangs in the air between them, filled by the howling wind, and then: 'I'm sure this is my seat,' responds the stranger inside.

'Hang on,' Bart rummages through the various pockets of his coat, sifting through napkins, old receipts, tattered fivers. He produces, at last, a crumpled piece of paper, works it flat with inflexible fingers and presses it against the window to be read, 'There, you see. Seat E16.'

Another pause hangs in the air. A distant bird caws; echoes.

Bart points impatiently through the glass, 'Look. In the ignition. My keys.'

The door opens abruptly, and someone climbs out, waving a crumpled ticket and mumbling, 'Sorry—I misread it. I'm F16.' The person heads off down the right-hand side of the road.

'Funny what a difference a little line makes,' comments the flea, chortling to itself. 'At least your seat will be warm.'

Bart climbs into the driver's seat, shuts the door, puts his seatbelt on and turns the key in the ignition. The choke of the engine fills the car, only to be drowned out by a chorus of shushing. He turns off the engine and shrinks down in his seat apologetically—a plastic bottle flies past his head and bounces off a seat a few rows ahead of him. Somewhere behind him, a voice lets out a harsh whisper, 'Quiet, quiet, it's starting!' An enormous screen lights up ahead as everything else is plunged into darkness. Bart's vision fills with bold, white lettering: 'BART, BRING MILK.'

The film shows a close-up of a woman's face, posed so that the yellow light of a fridge illuminates her features. Her mouth moves with a hint of disgust, corners downturned, and the voice itself seems mis-timed, as if dubbed.

'It's not good,' she says, enunciating every word as if her audience might struggle to understand otherwise, 'but not terrible. Once it's diluted in the cup, if I add a little strength, perhaps I won't be able to tell the difference.'

**

At the bottom of the ditch, a channel of water finds itself blocked by the body of a fox. It pulls in snug around the fox's shoulders, follows the curve of its back and the shape of its paws. A trickle breaks through beneath the hind leg and stumbles on.

A particularly green stalk of grass arches over the ambling rivulet and enquires, 'Where have you come from?'

The rivulet replies in a chorus of voices, all speaking at once and all saying different things. It gathers pace as the weight of larger streams pull in behind.

General unease sets in amidst the denizens of the ditch. An elderly groundsel rubs its roots and casts an anguished look skyward.

The water rises in slow increments, millimetre by millimetre. It tucks each of the fox's limbs into its belly, the sodden hairs forming smooth slipways along its surface. Cushions of water slip under it, scooping the foetal fox upward. Trapped gasses lend it buoyancy; it rises in a crouch, paws rolled underneath. It shifts downstream in stops and starts.

'Look at it move!' gasp a chorus of marvelling grasses, lining the bottom and sides of the ditch like spectators in a stadium. 'Where's it going?' Separate sections of the stands engage in different kinds of comment, some exclaiming wonder, others afraid.

'Watch it carefully,' murmurs the elderly groundsel to its comrades, 'Stay on your guard.' Grim nods of agreement.

The first eager rivulets fade from memory, engulfed by a great mass of water; trickling voices drowned out by the slow, booming sound of a single word, repeating like the low creak of a girder whose immense weight is spread over too great a length, 'Downstream,' it moans, '…downstream.'

***

Bold, white lettering onscreen, 'BART, BRING MILK' dim house lights brighten along the walls, and a general stir of rustling coats and bags erupts within the theatre. Bart finds himself hopelessly in the way of a group of people trying to exit the row and with no choice but to go with the throng downstairs, down a narrow corridor, and into a bright foyer. Walking silently amidst a buzz of excited chatter, Bart catches only fragments of conversations, words such as, 'composition,' and, 'lighting', and 'horror.' The bustle disperses throughout the high-ceilinged room, breaking and spacing out in groups of three or four.

The flea, having drunk its fill for now, reclines bloated amongst the fibres protruding from Bart's nape. The surroundings wash over its biconvex eyespots without much affect, for it is deep in thought, and troubled. As the fox's passenger, it had understood, more or less, how one thing proceeded another. There was a predictability about the life of that host that had made it comfortingly familiar. Simple habits, routines, repetitions. Rest, kill, eat. Rest, kill, eat. Rest, kill, eat. The blood of the fox had a different quality to it—it came thick, fast, fresh. Sometimes the fox's heart would beat so hard that the flea could've lost its grip. Danger, peril, survival! But this—this host—bleeds like water, its heart beats like a whisk.

Bart is embarrassed that he is the only one here not in conversation with a partner. He treads the foyer in a long circuit so that anyone who might happen to notice him would assume he was merely en route to a group he'd arrived with. On his way, he passes by a large, ebullient American who has the fingers of both hands wound up and stuck agonised through his beard, 'Not good, but not terrible,' he's saying to an enraptured gathering around him, 'An inability to tell the difference—am I making sense?' His final question solicits an applause of nodding heads and reassurances of, 'Oh, yes—I agree.' Someone offers him a handkerchief, which he uses to blot away the moisture on his face and neck. Onward, past a row of elevator doors, Bart notices a fringe group, orbiting a familiar sharp-faced woman—the star of the film—who smiles, embarrassed by the praise. A droplet runs down the bridge of her nose, hangs from the tip, then drops past her smile and onto the carpet.

Having completed a full circuit of the foyer, Bart plucks a colourful leaflet from a table and pretends to read it. Droplets of water smatter its surface. Ink residue stains his fingers. The thin paper sags and comes apart. Clinking metal and tapping plastic sounds out all around him and, looking up, he watches each person in the foyer open an umbrella. The ceiling lights illuminate a sloping drizzle of rain from ceiling to carpet. An announcement plays on the speakers and, arm in arm, the audience files back in through the corridor to the theatre with Bart amongst them, carpet squelching underfoot like sodden sponge.

The lights dim as stragglers crouch into seats. Chatter stops. The only sound is the rain pattering like applause off dozens of umbrella rooves. Bart blinks water from his eyes and huffs droplets off his lips, squinting to see the screen. Bold, white lettering, 'BART, BRING MILK'.

'What happened in the first part?' whispers the flea, covered from the rainfall by the lobe of Bart's ear. 'I didn't pay attention.'

It gets no response, of course. Bart focuses as the woman from the foyer—the film's star—appears on-screen rummaging through a cupboard in her apartment. She places a plain, white mug on the kitchen counter. Adds a teaspoon and a half of instant coffee. Fills two thirds with hot water. A slow, gentle stir. Her reflection is visible in the dark, swirling liquid, marred by the stain of a thin golden-brown crema. She sniffs the rim of a milk bottle, twice. Hesitates before pouring the milk in. The milk disappears into the black as if it were solid. The dark surface of the coffee, colour unaltered by the milk, sits prominently in the centre of the screen.

What's happening?' asks the flea, fixing its biconvex eyespots on the faces of the people around, noticing their suspense; their discomfort.

Slender fingers lower a teaspoon into the centre and gives the black, bitter liquid a stir. A loud, arrhythmic clinking of teaspoon against cup sounds out as the milk protrudes up to the surface in so many awful little chunks, the colour of yellow, sugar-bitten teeth. Bart can hear people squirming in their seats around him, umbrellas clinking. A warm, familiar hand from Bart's left side lands lightly on his knee and travels part way up his thigh, resting there. He draws a sigh of relief, turns his head, gazes past the empty passenger seat, through the ice-scarred windows, over the white fields rocking back and forth in the wind.

Between wildfires

Camara Fairweather

Siletzs Territory, Oregon, 1845

Adelaide stepped down from her horse and looked out across the open plains, but couldn't see anything more than dark outlines in the evening dusk. As she stood there, listening to the cicadas in the distance, a dry wind twisted dead leaves around her. The wildfire had died some days back. There were still embers trailing through the air, racing red and hot among the white ash.

'Steady now,' she said in a low voice, running a hand over her mustang's rosewood mane,feeling the soft touch of the brushed hairs passing between her fingers, 'I'll be back before long. Be good for me until then, okay?' She pushed her wide-brimmed hat back onto her head, gathered thereins, and with one last look to the horizon, set about tying her horse to the black remains of a tree.She wasn't exactly a Christian woman, nor was she the God-fearing type, but as the embers flamed and sawed beneath the evening sky, she couldn't help feeling as though she were staring at a scenefrom Revelations.

She lifted her father's double-barrelled shotgun from the leather saddlebag and turned it over in the half-light. She liked the way the gunstock rested in her arms. The weight of the wood.

The cold touch of metal against her skin. Made her feel alive to the narrow truths of the world. About the only thing that did anymore.

With a shallow breath, she broke the double barrel, chambered the ten-gauge rounds, and started down the trail. She moved slowly, staying close to the ground, a solitary figure against the dark and empty landscape. As she walked, she saw the carcasses of animals lying face down in thepale ash, smoke rising from their blood-black fur.

The dry river bed had once been home to freshwater fish. As a young girl, she had seen them swimming in the clear current and watched as their small fins weaved between the white edges of the water. The wind-kissed banks had been wet with honeysuckles and moss, sparkling in the low sun. It was there, among the deep green shade of the pines, that her father taught her to fire a shotgun. She remembered waiting, perched in the thickets, her father breathing over her shoulder, as she tracked a white-tailed deer between her cross hairs. She had moved instinctually—pulling the trigger in the space between heart beats—that short moment between breaths. The deer faltered and fell. She had skinned the animal later that morning, starting at the back legs, cutting along the tendons with the sharp edge of the knife. The muscles had a lot of gristle. It had taken her some time to saw through. When she had finished, her father had been so proud. Said she was a natural. He was dead now. Buried in an unmarked grave. Somewhere on the outskirts of Louisiana.

She thought about her parents as she moved deeper into the ashen valley, following the set of tracks drawn across the trail. Her father had been a slave. Her mother a southern belle. They had met on the bayou and spent the short time they had together out on a wide gallery porch under deep overhangs. Her memories of them were sun-bleached and faded. She found it hard to recall their faces. They drifted away from her reach, lost in the wind, like a dusty and half-remembered photograph.

After a while, the dead grass gave way to a small clearing out on the plains. A man growing into his later years was resting against the hard edge of a rock, warming his tired hands by a dying fire. Above him, hanging from the thin branch of a tree, was a lynched Native American man. His buckskin shirt ripped. His face paint scratched away. And the words 'red-skin' written across his body in blood.

'Hey there, old-timer.'

'That's far enough,' the man said in a whiskey-soaked velvet, hammering his .44 caliber revolver. He had a hard face. Smelt of cigar smoke and rough-hewn wood. 'Now, I've never really liked repeating myself so I'm just gonna say this one time. You come any closer and the next round I fire will be the last thing you see.'

'I know it's been a while but I figured you'd recognise me.'

'And why's that?'

'I'm a ghost from your past.' She said, stepping forward into the firelight with her shotgun holstered, the sound of her spurs carrying on the wind.

'Now, ain't that something. You're the little half-caste girl from Red River.'

'Yeah, well, not so little anymore.'

'You're a long way from home.' He took a drink from the barrel-aged whiskey in his left hand. Spilled some down his thick beard. 'What you doing all the way out here?'

'Thought the shotgun trained on you might speak for itself.'

'That a threat?'

'More of a promise.' She watched the old-timer's hand tighten around his gun. 'I'm thinking you probably don't remember that night or the way the wind howled across the empty fields. But I remember, young as I was. Pillowed there between my mama's arms. The cold turning my breath to steam. Sometimes I think about the stillness of those moments. The wild rabbits hanging on line, swaying softly above. So intimate and fleeting. Like the faintest whisper. Then I heard the sound of horses in the distance. Horses being ridden hard. The sound of their hooves cutting through the snow. The sound of riders dismounting. The sound of spurs outside the door. The voices of white men closing in. Heart pounding. Door not opening. Voices getting louder. Cursing outside. Mama telling me to be quiet. To hide under the bed. Daddy getting his shotgun. Kicking against the door. Wood splitting. Door breaking. Daddy being dragged out like a junk-yard dog. Mama screaming. The sound of a gun firing. Daddy's body hitting the ground. Birds scattering. Mama crying. Tears falling. Hands trying to stop the blood. Another gunshot. Then no sound. No sound but the wind.' She drifted away into silence, taking a quiet moment to breathe. The fire between them had burned to coals. It's warm light died before she spoke again, 'I still remember the last thing you said before turning tail. Said there are two kinds of people in the South. The quick. And the dead.' Her eyes narrowed. 'You want to know which I am?'

The old-timer moved to fire his gun. He was a fast draw—but Adelaide moved faster—firing the revolver out of his hand.

'That's right—' she said, staring down the smoking barrel. 'Now, raise your hands. Nice and slow, okay, old-timer? No sudden movements.'He raised his hands with some reluctance.

'All this for a cotton-picking nigger and a white bitch that couldn't keep her legs shut.' Adelaide back-ended him with the shotgun, bringing the blunt wood down across his face. Heard bone break as he staggered back, wounded and kicking up dust. He smiled through bloody teeth.

'Seems you got me at a disadvantage.'

'Don't smile at me because I'll rent that smile from your face.'

'I've never really given the words of women much credence, but I figure I'll push my chips forward. I've been at this a long time. I know a killer when I see one. And you ain't got the sand.' She pressed the shotgun barrel to his neck. 'Then you must not win a lot of poker games.' She said, exhaling sharply, and there was a cruelty waiting behind the dark and ghostly reaches of her eyes.

'Do you even regret any of the killings your gang of outlaws laid claim to?'

'No. I surely don't.' He said, spitting blood.

'That's funny. Because I don't regret killing any of your outlaws.'

She watched his face turn cold.

'You're lying.'

'Shot and killed every last one of them back in Albany.'

'That's a damn lie!'

'I think you already know it's not—' she said, pulling a six-shooter from her belt and letting it fall to the ground.

He looked down at the blood-rusted metal.

'That's my boy's gun.'

'Was.' She corrected him. 'That was your boy's gun.'

He held the revolver in his shaking hands.

'You're a rattlesnake on the trigger, I'll give you that,' he muttered darkly, 'but you've forgotten that the land beneath you is corpse white. And that ain't fixing to change. Even if you bury me and salt the grave, there's nowhere for you to run. This country is full of pitchfork and torches and as long as there are trees in the South, they'll be lynching black bodies from the branches. They can talk about giving you niggers rights. It don't matter. Those southern trees have deep roots.

Roots that spread in the dark. Been there growing since way before you were born. And they'll keep growing after you die.' He looked then to have the Devil in his bearing. 'You can try to run, rattlesnake, but you'll be impaled on those roots. And the birds will pick you clean.' She watched, through the pale and driftless smoke, as he aimed the revolver at her. His finger itched on the trigger, but she knew that he would never fire. There was only so much fight in a man and he'd lost his.

'You think I don't see you for who you really are?' She asked with a hollow inflection. 'All these years, I used to think you were terrifying. I'd wake up in cold-sweats, thinking about the violence you laid at our door, but I was wrong. Because you're not terrifying. In the end, you're just so small. I don't really give a damn if you think I've got sand. Your life ends now. You can say whatever you want. This cowgirl has heard it all before. All you can do is pray for a quick death, which you and I both know you ain't gonna get.'

He opened his mouth to say something cold and callous, but she cut him down before he had the chance. She stood over him as he clawed at his throat, reloaded, and shot two more rounds into his flesh. He died then and there. Looking down at the ground, Adelaide saw her reflection for the first time that night and recognised that something had changed within her nature. As she walked over the blood, back to her horse, she watched the reflection of the darkening sky ripple beneath her. She didn't know it then but there would be another wildfire in a few years. Summer after summer the sky would refuse to rain. The wildfire would cut through the plains, burning crops and trees and wiping away whole towns as though they were nothing more than tinder. Some people would burn alive. Others would suffocate from the inhalation of smoke. And many would run, leaving the lives they once knew behind forever. The wildfire would burn away all the cowboys hanging onto their fading way of life, as if they had never really existed, but Adelaide would remember.

Carousel

Migele Solano

Deliberating all your worries
insinuating bonfire brain-freeze
burning down 1000 bridges
rolling pebbles into ditches

calculating all your problems
line them all up and box them
make a folder of your x-rays
you're in a constant electric health craze!

take the sharp blade out your razor
become a spaceman shooting red lasers
take your toenails into town with you
let them see a sight outside of your shoe

start to worry about the climate
recycle your soul nobody will mind it
so so burdened with the world around you
you've lost your mind to the humming of the T.V screen
I'll be mean and I'll be me I'll be mean I'll be me
I'll be mean and I'll be me I'll be mean I'll be me

you're encompassed in deep anger
edges of your lips tied down with anchors
whatever I say misinterpreted
convert my words into something perverted

deliberating all your worries
forgetting about your human priorities
drunk in the spin of your carousel
life's a circus never a fairy-tale.

losing your faith in these humans
chewing them up, spit them out, use them
so so burdened with the world around you
lost your mind to the monotony of the reporters gleam.

I'll be mean and I'll be me I'll be mean, I'll be me
I'll be mean and I'll be me I'll be mean, I'll be me
I'll be mean and I'll be me I'll be mean, I'll be me
I'll be mean and I'll be me I'll be mean, I'll be me

Conrad Heard That Your Cat Died

Saskia Reynolds

Conrad Heard That Your Cat Died
How did he know before me?
Delete.

Something about Marmalade.
Marmalade
Marmalademarmalademarmaled
Marm
Fucking hell
Delete.

I remember the birthmark on your jaw because the last time I saw you, you were going up the escalator and I didn't want to stop looking at you and you were still facing me and fuck I couldn't stop so I stared until there was empty
Delete.

I don't want to write this, or anything like this. I don't want to cheapen anything between us; our relationship means a lot to me. But the itching at the back of my brain won't stop until I disembody us both, just enough that I can think about how much I love you without tainting it. This is especially hard to do whilst listening to a cover of '*Creep*' by Radiohead. The shadow of you in my mind makes my toes curl. There's something illicit here, although I hope our relationship is the purest, most innocent thing in the world. You could be a lot; you could be mother, sister, friend, teacher. I'm not quite sure. Perhaps that's where the unease comes from. I don't think that you are uneasy. Now or ever, I don't think uneasiness is within your capacity, as someone who someone like me loves to think about. Like taking purposeful slow time over playing a tune on the piano, I consider you. Every key is as important as the last. Like. I like you. I also like gentleness. Are you gentle? I think you like to rock my boat. You like to pry your fingers into my chest and hunt around with your fingers until you find something you can prod at, or perhaps caress. I am not like you, in that I am not a mysterious person. I don't think I was designed to be desired, which makes me sad. Retrospectively, when I feel myself writing these words, detaching you from you and me from me feels cold and harrowing somehow. But maybe if I desired myself a little more, I could be desired. I could be desired the same way I long for the warmth that comes out in the air between us during our conversations. For now, I will rest here, in the space between friend and child and adult. I will reside in the pleasure of your company, until you realise what I am, how far apart we are.

You mean everything to me. I know we don't really know each other like that but
Delete.

The air around you was the colour of her fur and I'm not being funny whenever we were close it's like the space around you burned, burnt orange and yellow and gold and I wanted to stay in your heat until you burnt the ground around us and there was nothing but this nothing but

Delete.

She was beautiful, I adored her. I really am sorry.

Delete all?

Save draft?
Subject heading?
Fuck you Conrad.
Backspace.
Subject heading?
Marmalade.

Dead Boys & Girls

Abby Nicole Greenwood

There are dead boys and dead girls
Walking around everywhere.

A dead boy meets a dead girl
When her hand falls off and he keels over to hold it.
A dead girl meets a dead boy
At a mixer for the demised and dateless.
They bond over him being buried
And her being burned.

The dead boy and dead girl decide
That the match of their decaying parts
Must mean the match of their decaying hearts.
As they do the Danse Macabre
Through the dying night
The dead boy and dead girl decide
That in death they shall permanently unite.

The dead boy watches the dead girl
Surrounded by their dead families
Make procession down the aisle.
They place their wicker rings
On their fourth metacarpal bones.

I promise to breathe in your ashes;
I promise to lie in your dust;
I promise to bathe forever in formaldehyde with you;
Until life tears us apart.

The dead boy and the dead girl
Move to the dance floor
For their first Danse Macabre
As dead husband and dead wife.
Everyone hears their dead hearts
Beat to the tune of the marche funèbre.
Decaying tears fall from dead eyes,
The perished pair being praised
For their dead love.

The dead husband carries the dead wife

Over the threshold of the first furnace of their very own.
They think of the dead boy and the dead girl
That will move through her like maggots,
They'll be different from us,
Our dead boy will be burned,
Our dead girl will be buried.

The dead dad and the dead mom
Teach their dead son and dead daughter
To do the Danse Macabre through the dying night
And tell them to find a dead boy or dead girl
To pick up and hold all of their decaying parts.

There are dead boys looking for dead girls to dance with.
There are dead girls looking for dead boys to die with.

Demons beyond the Door

Beth Lane

She, sunken eyes and hair like the twelve o'clock sea,
Biting rose quartz lips, pearl teeth, spilling bloody rubies.
Delicious quivers slithers sluggish around her bones,
They loom over her, eyes empty, as they grow and groan.
A crimson glow pulses, seeps from beyond the bordered glass,
Thin skin hangs from pallid fingers as they encompass
The coarse edges of the handle, hand melted into place,
Drip… Drip… Drip… A hushed scream paints her face.
Ink oozes between the dips of her digits, thick and hot,
Grappling, grasping, eager for her pasty skin to rot.
Strings dangle from her scrabbling arms, lug her across the floor,
Pitiful whimpers escape her mouth as she lurches from the door.
She plunges to the ground, gummy black smothering limbs,
She smears blood from her mouth, dribbles a thread of hopeless hymns,
Tastes frantic pleas to God on her tongue, along with salty tears
Blackness warps into hungry hands, moulding her gravest fears.
They loom, lanky lampposts, her feeble cry,
Stooping, keeping their heads from touching the sky,
Swinging low,
                                    cherry gaze,
Step closer,   her vision starts to haze,
One releases,   unbolts its mouth,
A terrible stream of nightmares
                              flows
                        south,
Her weary head whirls, they drag themselves nearer,
Bangs palms on the wall; is this all   her?
The door wheezes, spluttering out lumps of wood; it cracks,
Dark fingers burrow into her skin, clinging like blazing wax,
Her shriek,   curdling gore,
Snared by their hands,   nails tore
At chalk flesh,   throbbing red,
Door shudders,   black   pools   spread,
Wide eyes,   hanging limbs tread,
Thick liquid soaks, leaking to her head,
This is what   I always dread.
Suddenly her shriek falls,
Ribbons of outside sunlight sprawl,
Bare door flush against the wall,
Unblemished, no sign of them at all.

Depression Meals 101

Rose Ramsden

Go to switch on the kettle, then remember you haven't replaced the broken one yet. Begrudgingly take out a pot and fill it with water. Before, you would pour boiling water over ramen in a bowl, then place a plate on top. In the end, you find this new technique is worth the extra strain.

Pour some salt in the water so it boils faster. Or is it for flavour? Both? Either way, when cooking, salt is usually required, so sprinkle some in.

Berate yourself for not cooking a proper meal. Proper adults with proper jobs who properly contribute to society do not eat ramen for dinner at 11pm.

Remember the importance of three meals a day. There are no good foods or bad foods, there is simply food, which your body both needs and deserves. Alternatively, remember that multimillion businesses profit off your insecurity and eat out of spite.

Snap your ramen in two and put it in the pot once the water has come to a boil. Or put it in before. It probably doesn't matter.

Stir in the flavour sachet. Ponder whether chicken flavoured ramen means you're cheating on your new vegetarian diet.

Check the packaging and find out chicken broth is used to make the powder. Oh well, the world is dying anyway.

The packet says it takes four minutes to cook, but you like to be thorough, so stir for   eight and zone out for another two. You can be assured that it absolutely is not undercooked.

Turn off the stove. You can eat it from the pot, but if you like to lay down as you eat, a bowl is necessary to avoid burning yourself. If it's clean, use your favourite bowl. If you're feeling especially fancy, you can eat it with chopsticks. Leave the pot in the sink for three days before you finally wash it up. Eat and be pleasantly surprised that it's actually quite good. The static should subside at this point.

Well done. You're doing a lot better than you realise.

Disconnected

Beth Lane

"Hello?"

Swaying, sun-kissed branches darken his face with a veil of shadows; the sea, distant, reaches out for primrose sand, dulling its golden hue with frothy white waves. It is peaceful here, he notes; it mollifies his mind into almost forgetting the patient stranger waiting on the phone line. The stranger whose voice he would always recognise.

"I wanted to say congratulations." Silence. A hand—its quivering he has pointedly ignored—reaches up, jerks at the blackened tie that stifles him. Peering at the cloudless sky, he presses a finger against the apple in his throat. Of all days, today the sky does not bless the world with rain. He burrows a nail into milky skin, wondering if the sickly-sweet ache it brings will remind him this is reality again.

"Thank you, Viktor." That voice. Viktor's mouth fills with a bitter taste, as he feels his heart twist with treacherous yearning at its soft sound. "Although, I thought you would have congratulated us in person. Here. At our wedding."

Us. Our. What a joyful couple. He should not have dialled this number, yet the tiny white spring of hope that bloomed inside his chest had been his ruin. A foolish, fruitless hope; after all, what could an unwanted confession do?

"Ah, well, I couldn't…I can't…" He stares at his tie, elegant beneath a sprinkle of sand. "I couldn't get the time off work. My boss has always been unreasonable, you know that."

"It's a Saturday."

For a moment, Viktor contemplates swimming to the bobbing floats far out at sea, and simply laying there on his back, gazing at that bloody cloudless sky. He decides not to, of course. The waves, too passive, bashfully edge towards him and then retreat. In, and then out again. Viktor feels that, even if he stumbled to shoreline, even if he desperately stretched out, the pale ridges of the waves would never touch him. They would be so close, yet so out of reach.

That is how Elijah has always felt to Viktor: so close, yet so out of reach.

"Saturday? Oh, is it?" Viktor laughs; it sounds high-pitched and forced to his own ears. He grimaces, before rising from his spot, slinging his tie over one shoulder. "Overtime, then. The days at that place are all the same to me!"

"Right."

"God, I just realised the time. You must be getting ready for the ceremony! I should go."

"It's alright; I have a good few hours until it begins." That is a lie. Viktor knows because he has read the silver invitation a dozen times, until every line was seared into his memory, until it had crumpled to bits like dry leaves in his hand. Elijah's marriage to someone else is in an hour.

"How are you feeling?" Viktor continues the unwelcome conversation just to hear him speak, just to indulge in it for a minute more. He nears a coastal shop, where steaming chips fry in grease, an ample amount of powder stirs into a dense sauce, and beachgoers wait greedily, clothed in watermelon pink bikinis and immense straw hats. He peers inside with little interest.

"Cold feet?"

"Of course not!"

"Of course not." Viktor wants to scream; instead, all that escapes is a shuddering breath, as he narrows his eyes against the smarting gust of pungent vinegar that fills them with pools of salty tears. "I shouldn't have expected any less."

"Viktor—"

"You have always wanted to get married after all."

"And what about you? Have you found anyone special? Not to get married to, obviously. You have never wanted to get married after all." Elijah's spite is still present, and it stings Viktor in a way that feels nostalgic to him, an echo of what caused them to fall out of love. Or caused one of them to.

"Yes." No.

"Oh, wow, really?" Viktor delights in the change in his tone, so minute he would have missed it if he were not searching urgently for it.

"You sound surprised."

"I mean, I...I'm not. You're good, Viktor. It's a shame you couldn't have brought him to my wedding."

"You'll meet eventually."

"What is he like?" Before Viktor can answer, a sprightly, round-faced child accidentally tosses a semi-deflated, dotted ball at him.

"Sorry!" The shrill voice calls, sheepish, as Viktor boots it back over to him, grousing to himself about the beach's bustle.

"Viktor? Are you still there?"

"Yeah, sorry...Look, let's not talk about that. I'm calling to congratulate you on your wedding, not about me and my lover." Viktor burrows a polished shoe until it blends into the sand, before kicking up a sprinkle of yellow. Elijah takes a few beats to respond, as Viktor weaves in between throngs of people, keeping a leisurely pace as he heads towards his destination.

"Right. Yes. Not about you and your 'lover.'"

"Elijah…"

"Why aren't you here, really, Viktor?"

"I'm working. I told you that. Do you not believe me?"

"I don't have to. I can hear seagulls, and don't give me that bullshit that you're outside or something. Where are you? Why aren't you here?"

"Because…" I love you. I have never stopped. "I don't even know who you're marrying."

"It's on the invitation."

"Do you think I would remember that?" Viktor spots a grey cloud now, heavy and low. He hears a gentle patter on the surface of the soft sea, feels a damp pattern trickle down his temple, sees the frenzied rushing to shelter. He should have known. Viktor should have known that all pleasant things came to an end. Elijah was like a spell, a wish, beautiful but intangible.

"So, you aren't here because you don't know who I'm marrying. Do you know how bloody childish that sounds?"

"Almost as childish as you keeping everything about your fiancé from me until that invitation came through my door." All is subdued as tourists squeeze indoors, shoulder-to-shoulder, breaths entwined, unwilling to let even a dash of wet graze them.

"Jesus, Viktor. Do I have to fill you in on my love life? That's a bit inappropriate, isn't it?"

"You just now wanted me to fill you in about mine."

"That's…That's irrelevant! This is a fucking stupid reason to not come to my wedding. I spent half of my life with you, centralised around you, and you can't come see me on this one day?" Viktor pinches the bridge of his nose, before waving off a cherry-faced man, garbed in a florescent stripy vest, who beckons to a vacant dry space for Viktor to fill.

"Did you really expect me to come? We are past lovers."

"Of course I expect you to come; I want you to come. I still care for you." It brings an unwarranted tenderness that blooms in Viktor's chest; a warmth that is then doused in Viktor's own icy bitterness.

"It isn't about us or our feelings; you should know that. What would your fiancé think if I turned up?" The man frowns his bushy brows at Viktor, who is now cuddled by a layer of drizzle. "And no, I assure you, I am fine outside, please, take the spot for yourself. Thank you."

"Who are you talking to?"

"It doesn't matter. As I was saying, what would your fiancé think if I turned up? Why did you even invite me? We haven't spoken for…Christ knows how long,"

"I invited you because…Because," Viktor hears a burst of laughter, before a booming voice compliments Elijah's tailored suit. "Thanks, bud. Do you mind just giving me a bit more space? No, I won't be late, shut up! I'm just having a conversation with, uh…" It either drowns out, too faint, or Viktor stops listening, before Elijah addresses him again: "I wanted to see you again. I didn't like how we stopped talking, how it ended. I prioritised marriage over you."

"You wanted to see me again? At the very place your marriage is going to happen? The irony."

"Are you still bitter? Really? After all these years? Everything between us fizzled out long ago."

"Did it really?"

"What kind of question is that?"

"What kind of question was asking me if I had someone special?"

"What's that got to do with anything? I really don't have the patience for this right now. Just spit out what you want to say."

There, a faraway spot of colour, wooden chairs with ribbons of flowers snaked over the backs are scattered out, row after row, with a clear aisle of soggy, unturned ground. A dozen brollies that had been offered mask several frosty faces. They have not made a husband of Elijah just yet.

"Viktor? Hello?"

"Do you really want to know what I want to say?"

"As I said, just spit it out."

"Elijah, I...You know I have always been in love with you, even when you decided to leave. This whole thing is just ridiculous. Sending me an invitation to your wedding? After years of no communication? You think I'm just going to arrive and be all happy because of that? No. I can't. I won't. I won't do that to myself."

"What?"

"You heard it."

"You don't still love me, for God's sake, Viktor. We both moved on. Where is this coming from? This has got to be an excuse."

Viktor laughs sourly. He tilts his head up towards the misty heavens, allowing himself to pretend his tears are droplets of rain. He would never weep tears of shame. He would never weep for Elijah again.

"I still love you."

"Viktor. No. Stop this. You know this...You know this is stupid, yeah? You're lying. You're just feeling bad about not coming here, right?"

"Yes."

"Exactly. Good. Right. You don't love me. That was all a lie, wasn't it?"

"Yes."

"Good. Good. This is great! Fabulous! Isn't it?"

"Yes."

"You were really testing my cold feet there; you've always been clever. A good actor. You've always been too good."

"You should go, Elijah. Your wedding is soon." His voice is hollow, and the rain halts. Swarms of people scramble out, seeking sunshine; a few bounce and bump into Viktor with sleek surfboards tucked beneath their arms.

"Sorry! Didn't see you there!" Viktor does not reply, trudges on through what feels like metres tall of sand, and Elijah still yammers on in his ear.

"I don't know how it's going to go. It rained and then it stopped. I hope the sun stays out now. A beach wedding in the rain, ha! Imagine!"

"I'm sure it will be great."

"Yes, me too. I can't wait. I really love him, you know?"

"I know."

"He's amazing."

"You are going to be late."

"I'm sorry."

"It's okay. Be happy. Get married."

"I'm really sorry."

"Go to him, Elijah. You shouldn't be talking to me now; he's waiting for you."

"Viktor," Elijah murmurs his name, speaking delicately as though if he spoke otherwise, all would shatter. His sweet wedding, his future with someone else, would shatter.

"What? What more do you want to say? Is there anything left to say?" The poison that laces Viktor's tone, the pain messily shielded by rage, jolts even himself.

"No, you're right. Of course not."

The line goes dead. That was his final chance.

Viktor feels as if he is observing himself from afar, seeing himself with his big, round eyes sobbing big, round tears. Viktor sees himself as he gasps, snivels, his shoulders quaking with it, face twisted, fingers scraping at where his heart lays, pleading it to stop. He sees himself as he staggers, almost drunkenly, towards the alluring ocean that whispers sweet promises to him, sees himself as he is swallowed by white crests and green-blue peacefulness. But this is simply wishful thinking.

Instead, Viktor tightens his tie around his neck once more, and takes weighty steps, dripping droplets onto the golden ground, towards it. Towards the floral arch, where someone else waits for Elijah at the altar.

Eileen's Lemonade

Clarice Nicol

Eileen had always seen herself in Beyoncé. Of course, Beyoncé was thirty-four and Eileen was fifty. Beyoncé found her purpose in making art that made billions, while Eileen was a midwife. Beyoncé started having kids at thirty, and Eileen had her first at thirty-nine. But some dates did line up, like they had the same birthday, and in the same year Beyoncé and Jay-Z started dating, she and her husband got married. And, today, May 25th 2016, Eileen decided to watch Lemonade.

She had avoided Lemonade for one, very long month. She had dodged hot takes on Facebook, muted her friends' group chat so she wouldn't see Lemonade-inspired memes, and had all but cut off her cousin Sadie because Sadie could not help but try to spoil it for her every time they came into contact. The rest of the Beyhive had watched the film during its premier on HBO, but Eileen wanted to give Beyoncé's art the atmosphere it deserved. Only an evening alone, after a day off where she hadn't needed to do much, could suffice. This evening fitted those requirements. This evening, she'd watch it.

Or at least, she would, after the idiot truck driver in front of her finished reversing and turning and wriggling around in the tiny gap he'd trapped himself in. They were a few streets away from where she needed to drop Chelsea off at her sleepover, and she was already tired. By the time she got home, she might be too tired to even watch Lemonade. Then, she would have to wait weeks for another day off, and in that time, Sadie probably would have found an opportunity to run her big mouth.

She hadn't been in the best of spirits, sitting in her car for the past five minutes, wondering why this truck driver decided to go by this small side road and not the big high street that surely would have gotten him to where he needed to be much faster. She was irritated, had felt it build up at the base of her spine all day, and waiting for him and his incompetence to pass when all she really wanted to do was go home was just intensifying the feeling.

However, she hadn't become furious until he proceeded to slowly inch past her car, a few millimetres off from ensuring she'd need a new paint job.

"Oh," she said, her voice dropping in pitch, "You—F—"

She saw Chelsea staring at her through the interior mirror, wide-eyed, and then closed her mouth, swallowing the less-than-child-friendly rant she was about to embark on.

She wasn't sure why she was so volatile today. It wasn't like she'd had much to do that day to stress her out—she had fixed Chelsea's drawer, cleaned the house and did the groceries, but she also spent most of the day on her behind, watching television. In fact, yesterday she had been in much better spirits, when she'd gotten home after a hectic shift at the wards. She'd been running around in circles in her brain all day trying to identify the source of the feeling but that had led her nowhere. Now all she wanted to do was forget about it, drop Chelsea off at her friend's for her sleepover and finally get to watching Lemonade.

Luckily, the idiot truck driver finally managed to escape the tight space he'd trapped himself in and drove off. Somehow, the roads on the way to Chelsea's friend's house and on her way back home were surprisingly empty. Her spirits lifted a little when she arrived at her empty house, and the quiet made her shoulders relax. She hadn't even noticed they'd been tense all day.

It was night, the best time of the day. She changed the bedsheets, showered, put on her favourite lotion, and slipped into her most expensive pyjamas. She dimmed the lights. She lit a candle. Her laptop was fully-charged. She had already downloaded Lemonade that morning. Unlike most of the things she watched or listened to, she had paid money for it too.

And she watched it.

And hated it.

There was something not quite right about the film that reminded her of when she went to see her cousin Henry's choir and that one bass weaved in and out of being on and off-key. It exacerbated the strange feeling of irritation that had been following her around all day. Especially the random appearances of Beyoncé in a wedding dress, the exposure turned up to the point where her skin looked white, wearing long weave. That particular image wouldn't leave her mind, not even when she settled into sleep.

In her dream, Eileen found herself fumbling for a shirt and a skirt from her wardrobe. Her phone, which she paid way too much money for, had not woken her up. She remembered this scene from this morning. In a few seconds, her husband would wonder in, grabbing his cufflinks and fixing them to his shirt, and she would turn on him with a glare. He had also allowed her to sleep in.

"Why didn't you wake me?" Eileen felt herself say to him, as he made his way to the drawer that his cufflinks sat on top of.

Her husband glanced up, momentarily, as he had that morning, before returning to fiddling with his shirtsleeves. "It's your day off."

Her arm reached for her phone, opening it. Below the time, was the date: Weds, 25th May. It was her day off.

Her body sank down onto the bed, a hand swiping over her face. "Sorry. That was uncalled for."

When they first got married, he said one of the reasons he loved her was how put together she was. She used to have action plans, spreadsheets and folders full of research for everything. Back then, she organised their finances into a system which made sure that they had enough money to live on for a whole year saved in an emergency fund. She planned and cooked every meal they had ahead of time, every single one healthy and nutritious. She had not spent as much time as him worrying when he changed careers, hadn't done as much snapping as he did when he was rejected from the first few employers on his job search. She hadn't needed to. She had planned for it and had six different back up plans, in fact.

He used to say she grounded him when his worries got the better of him. She wasn't sure what had happened in the last six years, but he never said that anymore.

Through the corner of her eye, she thought she saw a woman in a wedding dress, looking ready to jump at any chance to help, to give, a smile plastered onto her face. She felt a tingle at the bottom of her spine. When she turned to look, the woman had gone.

Her husband brushed his hand over her shoulder. "It's okay." he said, before going downstairs to do his usual routine of getting the kids in order and coming back to give her a hug.

After he left, her body shifted into the rhythm of cleaning the house, and then repairing Chelsea's chest of drawers. Finally, after her body finished, it went into the shower and put on some clothes.

Her eyes glanced at the mirror after she finished dressing.

Her braids stuck up at odd angles. Her grey hairs had become much more noticeable these days. Her older sister had solemnly recommended a hair brand to cover it up. Her aunt had volunteered to dye it for her, saying that it looked messy on her; that it wasn't appropriate for work, especially if she insisted on wearing her hair like that, without relaxing it. She had caught some of her colleagues eyeing her hair warily, as if they thought she would soon administer the wrong injection to the wrong patient, on top them thinking she might arrive at work with the smell of weed stuck to her clothes.

A dark lock of a straight, understated wig brushed against her shoulder, the kind her aunt would have wanted her to wear. The woman she saw in the mirror positioned her head next to hers, eyes lined with a respectable amount of black eye pencil, her lips red. Her skin didn't look real. It was three or so shades lighter than her's and so smooth and shiny it reminded her of a porcelain doll. There was not a single hair out of place. Other than that, she looked exactly like Eileen. The feeling at the base of her spine grew. She wondered what her aunt would say if she looked like that.

Eileen turned to face her.

She was the only one in the room.

Her body reached for the TV remote, searching for mindless entertainment. It settled on the Real Housewives of Atlanta. The women on it were all hourglass shapes and long legs. She used to look like that. But after two babies and the onset of her fifties, she couldn't seem to get it back, no matter how hard she tried. She saw a woman out of the corner of her eye. She was slim and tall and curvy, wearing a straight wig. She wore Eileen's clothes. Eileen blinked, and she was gone. She switched the channel to a rerun of Mrs Brown's Boys.

At one her body got into the car and went to the supermarket, and while she was there, Eileen felt the security guard's eyes boring into her. To be fair to him, she had been staring at the same box of lemons for longer than she probably should, deciding whether she should buy some or not. She was also wearing one of her old hoodies. She remembered it was something that she would rather not have worn that afternoon, but it was unexpectedly cold, and it was the only jumper she had with her.

Out of the corner of her eye, Eileen saw a woman. Quiet red lips. That same straight wig. She was wearing a cashmere jumper, a silk scarf tied around her neck, three-inch heels. The kind of outfit that, perhaps, would stop the security guard from looking at her the way he did. The feeling at the base of her spine became more insistent.

Eileen turned to face her.

There was no one there.

At the school, Chelsea ran up to her and burst into tears, mumbling about a toy that had been confiscated from her. She tried her best to comfort her, but Chelsea just cried harder, and she felt the other parents and some teachers turn to watch her. Off to the side, she thought she saw a face like hers, a few shades lighter, twisted into the most perfectly understanding smile, the kind that probably would have helped Chelsea calm down faster. The feeling at the base of her spine became almost unbearable.

She stood back up after Chelsea had stopped, and turned, but the woman wasn't there.

She found herself in the car, in traffic, with a song, "Don't Hurt Yourself" prodding her in the back of her mind, like it was trying to get her to see something.

Images of the woman who looked like her flickered in the interior mirror. She felt the dream collapse around her, "Don't Hurt Yourself" merging into "Flawless", her alarm.

As she felt herself wake up, she decided Lemonade was a good album after all.

Identity Crisis

Alex Grenfell

INT. G-9682'S OFFICE, G DIVISION PROCESSING—DAY
G-9682, a man wearing white overalls with a shaved head, upon
which there is a sticker of a barcode, sits behind a white
desk in his office.

A loud buzzer sounds. G-9682 presses a button on his desk.
G-0213, an almost identical copy of G-9682 wearing a similar
barcode, shaved head, and overalls, enters. Unlike G-9682,
G-0213's mannerisms are nonchalant; he hums and walks in with
his hands in his pocket.

G-0213: Alright, Dez?

G-9682: We've been over this, G—um—G-0213?—You must now address me as G-9682.

g-0213: Alright, Dez.

G-9682: Just—just take a seat.

G-0213 sits opposite G-9682.

G-9682: Right, well, G-0213, I've called you in here because
we need to have a serious discussion about your conduct—

g-0213: Look, Dez, just because I've been calling people by
their real names—G-9682: Their identity numbers are their
real names.

You know very well it's now Central State law to refer to
individuals by their assigned identity number; the number
relegated according to caste, position, and—

g-0213: Wait, since when?!

G-9682 sighs loudly.

G-9682: Have you not been following the news at all?

g-0213: Nah, not really, Dez. (Beat.) I mean, I was following
it when the State made me shave my head and wear these dodgy
overalls, but then I kinda got bored.

G-9682: That was over a year ago!

G-0213: Yeah... it was pretty wank really, it turned me right off all that propaganda jizz. (Beat.) So, if we've all got these new names, uh—

G-9682: (Through gritted teeth.) State assigned registration numbers.

G-0213: Yeah! Those! How do I see what mine is?

G-9682: Why the fuck do you think it is now the law to wear a fucking barcode on your head?

G-0213 shrugs.

G-0213: Uh… the Director's got interesting fashion sense?

G-9682 sighs.

G-9682: You do realise I should have you re-educated just for that comment, right?

G-0213 shrugs again. Pause.

G-9682 (Cont'd): Look, G-0231—I mean, G-0213—you're not a good fit for G Division. You're nearing the bottom of the bar-rel of the G's—I mean, you've attained rank 0213, for crying out loud.

G-0213: No way! That's my rank! That's great!

G-9682: No, it is not "great"—the lower the number the poorer the performance—

G-0213:Bollocks, it's, like, a countdown, innit, Dez. How do I have a look?

G-0213 takes off his barcode and squints at it.

G-9682:For the State's sake, put that back on! You have one of the worst ranks this side of the State, G-0213, and, frankly, you're deserving of it. I've filed the paperwork that'll have you re-educated, effective immediately—

G-0213 quickly jumps at G-9682, and peels off the barcode sticker off his head.

G-9682: What are you doing?!

G-0213 and G-9682 fight each other to the floor. The buzzer rings again. G-0213 hits G-9682 very hard. G-9682 writhes on the floor in pain as G-0213 puts G-9682's barcode on his head, cheering.

G-5373, a female worker sharing the characteristic shaved head, barcode, and overalls, enters.

G-5373 (Cont'd): Hi, sir. I know you probably don't remember me, but I'm G-5373 from the ectogenesis laboratories, we had a little problem with womb production—

G-5373 notices G-9682 writhing on the floor.

G-5373 (Cont'd): What in the State's name is going on?!

G-9682: Help—!

G-0213 steps on his throat, silencing him. He tries to imitate G-9682's voice.

G-0213: Another terrorist attempt, I'm afraid! He tried to steal my precious barcode!

G-9682: L—liar—

G-0213: Shut up!

G-5373: His voice—

G-0213: I know. Likely a trained, um… impersonator? Yes… uh, bloody revolutionaries.

G-0213, foot still on G-9682's neck, relaxes down into G-9682's chair. He presses one of the buttons on the desk.

A loud siren blares.

G-0213: Oh—that wasn't—uh, don't mind that! So, you're G-5373 from ectogenesis, right?

G-5373: Yes... yes, sir.

G-0213: So, there must've been a problem with, like, baby-making then?

G-5373: Child-manufacturing, yes—

G-9682: Please—I'm the real

G-96—G-0213 applies more pressure to G-9682's neck, quietening him again.

G-0213: Don't mind that! So, what happened, G-5—um…

G-5373: G-5373, sir. Well, it wasn't my fault—G-5374 was too busy reading censored books to— Two heavily-armed figures in faceless, armoured suits barge into the office. An OFFICER points at G-0213.

OFFICER #1: Up. Now.

G-0213 calmly rises, releasing the gasping G-9682.

G-9682: What—officers—?

OFFICER #1: Right, present your barcodes for scanning, please.

OFFICER #1 takes out a device that resembles a breathalyser and puts the nozzle against G-5373 and G-0213's barcodes. The OFFICERS gruffly nod as the device pings, then turn to the barcode-less G-9682, still lying on the floor.

OFFICER #1: Where's your barcode?

OFFICER #2: What in the State's name are you doing without a barcode anyway? It's the bloody law you bleeding loon!

G-9682: No—you don't understand—

OFFICER #2: Oh, I understand bloody well enough—under the law, if you're not wearing a barcode, you must be one of the terrorists!

G-9682: No, no—he took it—

G-0213: No, I did not! He willingly took off his barcode and tried to take mine. Luckily, I, um, subdued this terrorist…

G-9682: Don't believe a word he says! I'm the real G-9682! I'm a very important man!

OFFICER #2: Shut it, terrorist!

The OFFICERS both grab G-9682, who struggles against them.

G-9682: No—what are you doing?—I told you—I'm G-9682—please—I'm Desmond Adley—I'm friends with the Director—

G-0213: How dare you! G-0213 slaps G-9682.

The OFFICERS drag G-9682 out, still yelling.

G-0213 (COnt'd):Typical revolutionary! Trying to, um, manipulate me—yes—by using my disgusting birth name rather than the, uh, the freedom of my State provided registration number… um, well you're dismissed, G-5373.

G-0213 walks to the desk and sits, relaxed, hands behind his head and feet up on the desk.

G-5373: Really? So, what—no consequences?

G-0213: Uh… no. It's been a very stressful day, I can't really be bothered with all the filing, to be honest.

G-5373: Thank you, sir.

G-0213: Don't mention it!

G-5373 bows, then hesitates. Pause.

G-0213: Well? What are you waiting for?

G-5373: Nothing —it's just you're—you're not usually this nice, sir.

G-0213: I'm trying to turn over a new leaf, don't make me regret it.

Another long pause.

G-5373: Okay then, can I get a promotion?

G-0213: A promotion?!

G-5373: Yeah—I think I deserve to be G-5374. Maybe G-5474 while we're at it, sir. Although let's be honest... you're not really G-9682, are you?

Pause.

G-0213 shrugs, then smiles sheepishly and speaks with his old voice again.

G-0213: Alright—you got me. Congratulations, G-5474. Promotion well earned.

G-5373: Thank you, sir.

G-5373 exits, grinning.

G-0213 spins around childishly in G-9682's chair, celebrating.

Fade Out:
the end

Existentialism

Libby O'Reilly

These shattered shards we call memories,
those quivering vertebrae of life,
the moment we stare into the mirror
and with breath realise we are breathing,
oscillating through time and space
until suddenly we are not.
We are fragments of the earth,
minerals incarnate, loving and
bursting with emotion—a battery
that runs until the last drop is gone,
then what do we have to give
but the threads of our past—just
moments of recovered memory, of so called
nostalgia. Pictures, smells or a familiar sound.
We stare down at sun warped hands,
smiling with a melancholy that says:
I have lived, yes. I was young, once. But time
has escaped through the gaps in my fingers,
I let it pass as unconsciously as the landscape
from the train window that slides from view.
Cherish each mortal breath you take
and let the world take it from you.

Final Approach

Cathy Sole

Greasy chips
And sides of lips
Sweat in hot-boxed silence.
Dark and peripheral
Dreams are lost in wing mirrors,
Caught in vague horizons
From the rear-view.
We drive but never move,
Then fly, flung from the windscreen.

Crashing into you is grounding.
Salt-licked-fingertips scratch
At yellow-smoked-skin
That I will cling onto for dear life.
What's unsaid is too hard to swallow.
Like a ball of potatoey chips,
Stuck until you comment on the weather.
Trample a fag butt,
Birthing a snowdrop.
Gaze at passing pigeons,
Turning them doves.
Seagulls-turned-swans
Are suspended in mid-air,
Flying perpetually.
We've all gotta land.

Flesh and Blood

Cathy Sole

If I'm unfeeling,
You're the cold snap
That froze these sinewy cogs.
If I'm a blister,
You're the needle that
Never let my skin callous
And flooded us both in
Embryotic fluid to ease
Our symbiotic joints.
I am not your creation
But I cannot deny we
Are made of the same stuff
And I don't know what scares me more:
That part of you is me or part of me is you or how
We are made from the same stuff as scars.

You are the scab that never stops scabbing.
A cracked heel that never softens.
A clockwork gear in an automatic car
And if you ever see me on a train
And you're standing outside the train,
Don't wave.

Diana

Cathy Sole

Weak wrists,
Strong fingers.
Always tapping and touching and caressing and clinging,
Like you're a mast and I'm
Sailing this raft through
Jam-packed hills of compounded snow.
But not matter how slowly I go
I always end up on my knees.
Like a bandy-legged deer I scramble to stand
Like skating backwards on ice, but I go
Nowhere.

I broke my arm when I was out skating
In a hilarious freak accident. Limbs all over the place.
I would've told you but

A deer is skittish and pretty and claims
Prairie white fields as home.
Don't try and catch her
For she is a wild thing,
Prancing through yesterday's snow.
Just let her go.

First Place Your Name Between Your Teeth
Rowena Price

Before they are heard, names are to be tasted, mapped with gentle scrutiny of tongue, swilled to separate grain from colour. Names that swell perfumed like a fig in your pig mouth. Names that sit steaming in the throat and pepper the lungs or slide out when you are not expecting it. Names that are their own internal truth cannot lie. Rosemary is one of these. Rosemary sitting under a tree with your head in my lap, Rosemary saucepan steam circles your shoulder, Rosemary pearls and silver bells in your hair. Noble names, salty names, close the shutters names, names in heavy oak and names engraved in gold. Good names for a cow. Elijah Bryony Ines Rory: stand tall with your back straight. Lucy: a tiny seashell beaten to translucence by waves. Penelope: I left the cardboard recycling out in the rain. These are not observations but textures. My lover's name is meeting me in the field your hands are bigger than I remember and smell of moss and garden endeavours. Rough vegetable dampness. Wearing your socks into the bathroom, you stand in the puddle of water by the sink. Oil rests above water and starlight is old. A name you cannot pronounce is in the wrong mouth. Your name on new lips is bread still warm from the oven. Are you the hot skin of coagulated custard or the drawers are jammed full of old papers? Do you know? Have you ever asked? Do not leave your name lying on the floor. If it was given to you but is not yours, you must carve out your own. Every year you pass the day of your death without knowing, so place your name between your teeth and spit out the sounds you like best.

Footprints in the Fog

Chris Bowler

You run blindly through grass,
panting hard, breath
cut to pieces by cold
morning air. The fog
lies all around you, no path
in sight. Cold spots of light

filter towards you, a light
that watches footprints appear beside you. The grass
lies silently, watching you stumble away from the path.
You sigh, watching your breath
float upward, past the fog
and the waves of cold

that try to drag it down. The cold
sneers, and closes in further. The light
watches on, through the tinted haze of fog
that floats just above the grass.
Still standing, you catch your breath
but don't see the footprints appear behind you. A path

floats in front of your tired eyes, a path
wrapped in silver and framed by cold
limbs and aching lungs. Shivering, your breath
catches in your throat. Eyes straining, you watch the nearest light,
floating inches above grass,
coming closer through the dense fog.

You'd forgotten about the fog.
Eyes darting, you search for the path,
but lonely eyes find only more loneliness in the grass.
Panicking, you stare directly at the cold
white mass that lies in front of you, finding eyes of light
staring back. Your breath

starts to quicken, a shallow breath
that had just seen the footprints in the fog
lying ahead of you, pointing into the light.
They lie, unmoving, promising a path,
offering shelter from the cold.

The footprints beckon, lying in the grass.

Your breath starts to quicken, the hope of a path
spurring you on. The fog wraps its arms around you, and the cold
floats down, settling in front of your face. Light shines on footprints in the grass.

Grandma

Oliver Shrouder

I

Sensing something was missing
I called Grandma at the home;
she answered on the eighth ring with a low
ee-e-e-eeh and *hello, dear, what's the matter,*

I couldn't tell her, so I said *how have you been?*
I heard her smile, shift in the chair she fell into
fifteen years ago where her muscles melted
into the folds. *Same old thing, she says,*

I finished one of my puzzles, only took an hour,
I said *mhm,* this was her third time completing it—
When did I get so old? she asks herself
You're as young as ever I say and she laughs then goes silent

It's nice to hear a new voice sometimes (I heard her
move to look down at her phone) *James*
I said *me too* and a third voice said
come on now Deirdre you can't sit all day

she says ee-e-e-eeh hello dear and she is gone.
I am twenty-one today. Her last card came two years ago
three months early saying *dear Tony.* Mum asked
who's Tony? laughing, then later crying *who's Tony?*

II

Grandma is eighty-six today. Someone at the home
has taught her how to video call and she smiles
down with her chin out, doesn't say anything.
We are all quiet; maybe nothing has happened.

I remind her she is eighty-six; she says *blimey,*
that's old, and looks worried until she looks outside:
her face calms as she counts the gulls.
Mum says it's been tough being stuck inside.

Grandma points to a picture of a man on her bedside
and calls him pretty, thinking it must be an actor
she once loved. Mum agrees, Dad leans in

and I squeeze into frame; Granddad smiles from his.

Next year Grandma will be eighty-seven
in the same chair and I hope we can visit then.
Someone needs to tell her it's her birthday;
she looks away to count the gulls
but they're silent, and there every day.

Get over it

Denise Monroe

She had been putting it off all week. Ending it, that is. It had really run its course. She knew that they both knew it but also that neither of them wanted to be the one to do it. Finally, yesterday, she had messaged him: can we meet?—sure—Tate at 12?—cool. She had regretted it immediately. The Tate had been where they had met so really it was a bit crass to end it there. He probably thought it was a romantic gesture and it was all going to be fine. Still, it had to be done.

She wheeled her bike through the kitchen and into the hall and wondered if he would cycle too. Probably. That was one of the things that had drawn them together. Midnight bike rides though the city, the lights of Hoxton, the smell of beer and the jostle of crowds on the pavement outside The Crown on Curtain Road. She put on her helmet and freewheeled down Camberwell Grove, past the old swimming pool and their favourite falafel shop on the corner of Church Street. Her breath caught in her chest, an almost imperceptible gasp, and she wondered if she would ever eat there again.

She was early, always early, she couldn't help herself. It went back to when she was small and dependent on her mother to deliver her to parties and friends' houses and schools and hospital appointments. Then, she was always late and lived in perpetual fear of entering rooms to the glare of friends and teachers and doctors. That was why she cycled the city so as never to be at the mercy of bumpered traffic on the Walworth Road or the unreliability of the ancient Northern Line.

She made a detour via London Bridge just so she could cycle through Borough Market, past the Monmouth coffee shop that served their favourite flat white. It was as though she had to make herself suffer before inflicting pain on him. She hadn't planned to stop but was drawn to the window by the smell of coffee, like burned amber. Amber was the colour of his eyes. She was upset to see another couple sitting at their favourite table; holding hands, smiling, sipping coffee. A reminder that life would go on.

She turned away and pushed her bike through the market, tried to focus on what to cook for supper. She hadn't been vegetarian until she'd met him, convinced by his argument and pleading puppy dog eyes. It struck her that she could now eat meat again, if she wanted. Perhaps she should have a celebratory meal of chicken to remind herself that she was free, her own person again. But when she stood at the butcher's counter all she could see were the carcasses of dead things: muscles and sinew and splintered bone. As the metallic scent of blood filled her nostrils, she felt nothing but nausea and pity and realised that she might, indeed, be over it. She nudged past the shoppers and clipped her shin on the pedal of her bike. She should really lock it up but didn't have much time and all of the lamp posts had been occupied on Stoney Street. Perhaps just some bread and eggs would get her through what was bound to be a difficult evening.

She chose a small sourdough and bent to her panier to rummage for her purse.

It was then that she saw him, through the gap between the stalls. She'd forgotten how handsome he was. Over the last week she'd only thought of his failings: the fact he was always late, his refusal to wear the leather brogues that she preferred, his preference for Builder's over Earl Grey. He was smiling at the girl who was serving him at the flower stall. She loved that about him—his ability to talk to anybody, to make them feel at ease, to charm and be friends with them. She was never jealous but rather basked in the warmth of his smiles, knowing that they were really hers, that she was sharing them with the others.

The girl handed him a bunch of cornflowers and she remembered that she had once told him how their shocking violet blue reminded her of her dad's eyes. He was good like that, at getting the little things. She almost called out to him but stopped herself; she wasn't ready yet. They weren't due to meet for thirty minutes and she needed that time to prepare. She left the bread unbought and backed out of the market. The flowers confused things.

She locked her bike outside the gallery and rode the escalators to the fourth floor. There was time. The higher she went the more clearly she could see the macabre fountain installed in the Turbine Hall. The twisted faces of sharks and gargoyles snarled up as if chastising her for what she was about to do.

There was no one standing in front of their painting. 'Source,' it was called and they had joked about it being the source of them; their beginning. Once again, she examined the lines and dots that swam before her. The sperm heads looked as soft as black velvet with their central eyes like seeds of interrogation, the black tails a network of lines that trapped the delicate yellow dots in the petri dish. She had felt like that, herded and corralled into the expectation of reproduction. That's what she'd told him the first time they'd stood here. She had been so engrossed in the pattern on the canvas that she hadn't seen him behind her, had stood on his shoes as she tried to get a wider perspective on the painting. She had blushed and he smiled and they'd spent the rest of the afternoon together, wandering the galleries and talking about art and then film and then cycle routes and then food.

Now she looked at the heads and the tails of the painting and, where once she had seen a cold search for a partner, she saw affection. The seed heads that had found each other were nuzzling, not prodding, and the lines of entrapment now seemed as sure as an embrace. She felt confused at her interpretation, so sure had she been of her need to be separate.

She sensed him before she saw him. Perhaps it was the crinkle of the paper-wrapped flowers or maybe it was the smell of him: a mixture of sandalwood and city streets, earthy and fresh, solid and free.

Hi, he said.

You found me, she said back.

They stood together silently, examining their painting. She leaned her head onto his shoulder before she even considered that it might be the wrong thing to do. She was unsure of who she was, of what it was that she wanted; of whether she ate meat anymore, whether she preferred tea laced with bergamot over the tannin of PG Tips, whether North London was better than South.

For you, he said and offered the flowers to the line of her eyes. He kissed the top of her head and she felt complete. I love you, he said.

She breathed in the sweet scent of the deep blue flowers and remembered the smiling florist. I know, she said. Shall we get coffee?

How to Disappear

Denise Monroe

'You're not going until you've finished.' Mum watched and Poppy pretended to chew on the pasta that was slowly congealing on the plate in front of her. 'Have you got your snack for later?'

'You should know, you packed it.' Poppy wanted to scream but managed to keep to sarcasm, buoyed by the knowledge that she would ditch the biscuit in the first bin she saw.

'Are you sure you'll be alright having breakfast at Anna's?' Mum turned to take a yoghurt from the fridge which gave Poppy just enough time to slide the last of the pasta into her pocket. Why wouldn't she shut up? Stupid cow. All the woman thought about was what the next meal would be and what was for pudding and not to forget her late night snack. Mum swapped the plate for the pot and sat across from her daughter. She smiled tightly with her mouth but not at all with her eyes. Poppy felt sick at the sight of the yoghurt but was smart and knew that if she couldn't control what went down, she could decide what came back up. She held her breath and swallowed the slimy pudding.

Finally free, she slammed the front door with half a goodbye. She heaved her rucksack onto her back and the sneaky hip flask clanked against the cans of Diet Coke that Mum had given her. Anna had said to meet at six and it was already half past five. Poppy hated being late and have everyone stare at her when she arrived: much better to arrive early and be the starer.

She ran from the bus stop all the way to the Southbank. Anna was already talking to a bunch of boys and Poppy slowed down in the hope that her flush would fade before she joined them.

'Sorry I'm late,' she tried to sound cool but was boiling inside.

'Are you?' Anna flicked her sleek blonde hair with a roll of her head and smirked at the tallest boy. 'I hadn't noticed.'

They made a gang and walked along the crowded embankment. Poppy handed the rum to Anna and admired her long, slender neck as she tipped it back and swallowed. She tried to do the same but her throat automatically clenched against the alcohol and she spluttered it into her hand. Anna smirked at the boy again and Poppy coughed to hide her shame.

They sat on a concrete curve to watch skateboarders show off. One of the boys put his arm around Poppy's shoulder and leaned in for a clumsy kiss. His breath smelt like cheesy Wotsits but she let him poke his tongue in her mouth anyway. He wiggled it around a bit and she swallowed a gag.

'This is boring,' Anna stood up and smoothed her short tartan skirt over her thighs. 'Let's go to mine.' She led the way and leant into the tall boy who hooked his elbow around her neck in a hold that was more like a grip than a grope. The two other boys, little and large, fell in step behind the leaders, hands in their pockets desperately trying to look like they didn't mind being the odd ones out.

Poppy and Wotsit boy lagged behind. He held her awkwardly about the shoulder so she couldn't move properly and had to look at their feet to try and establish a matching march. She didn't see Anna or the boys in front of her stop and so walked right into the back of the skinny one. She lifted her head with a start and knocked Wotsit boy in the chin as the coke cans shuddered in her rucksack and across her bony back. He released her in order to rub the pain and complain while Poppy pretended to be fine.

Anna was pointing into the shadows under the concrete mass of the theatre and it took a few seconds for Poppy to figure out what was there. Then she saw them, almost hidden but not quite. A wave of nausea rose from her gut and threatened to spew onto her tatty white Converse and the ground that was now spinning beneath her.

'Isn't that your mum?' Anna almost sounded like she cared.

Poppy slapped her hand to her mouth as the familiar taste of bile clawed its way up her gullet. They were all looking at her now and she felt the expectation of a reaction. She didn't know whether to laugh with them or to make a scene or to brush it off with indifference so she did what she always did when things got difficult. Panicked. She pushed past Anna and her pretence of concern and ran until she knew she was out of her sight. Only then did she slow to a march and process what she had seen. Mum. Kissing a strange man. It was disgusting. Poppy knew that Dad was a prick but that didn't mean Mum could go around with other men. The bile bubbled inside her again but she swallowed it down; it could wait. She pushed her hands deeper into her jacket pocket and tried to quiet the voice in her head but it kept on at her. It was all her fault, she should never had eaten that pasta.

As soon as she got home Poppy ran up the stairs, reached for the toilet seat and vomited her disgust out. It tasted of rum and cheese and she felt even more nauseous so she shoved her fingers down her throat just to make sure there was nothing left inside. It burned but it was what she deserved.

Later, in bed waiting for sleep, she heard the scratch of the key as it searched for the barrel and the familiar creak of the front door that no one could be bothered to oil. Then voices: his and hers. Mum laughed, a noise almost forgotten, sweet and trill and edged with happiness. It made Poppy hate herself even more. The tread of footsteps on the stairs, her parent's bedroom door closing with a soft click, the harmony of two voices as they danced with each other and then, the fumbling silence. She reached for her headphones and the scissors that were hidden under her mattress.

In the morning Poppy clattered around in the kitchen as loudly as she could. She banged a frying pan onto the cooker and fried the bacon hot and hard. She raised her arms above the pan to crack an egg into the sizzling fat and made sure that it splashed onto her already burning skin. She whizzed up a smoothie, long and loud, and clattered the dishes away.

A floorboard creaked in the room above and shushed voices tripped down the stairs. Poppy slammed a knife and fork onto the table, tipped the greasy bacon and eggs onto a plate and angrily smeared toast with a thick layer of butter. The front door closed quietly and a smile stretched over her perfectly white teeth.

'You're home early,' Mum picked up the kettle and walked to the sink, her eyes focussed on anything but Poppy.

'I didn't stay at Anna's.'

'What do you mean?' The kettle stalled under the tap and water overflowed the spout.

'What I said.' Poppy scraped the chair out from under the table and sat down with a thump.

'You came home last night?'

Poppy poured herself a tall glass of smoothie. 'That's right.'

Mum fumbled the kettle into its stand and cautiously approached the table. 'What time did you get home?'

'Early.' Poppy pushed the plate of food away from her as Mum perched on the chair and pulled her dressing gown closed across her chest.

'How could you Mummy?' Poppy watched with satisfaction as the dim glow of happiness drained from her mother's eyes. She put the food bin on the table and slowly lifted its lid, releasing a tiny cloud of fruit flies. Normally she secreted her food away when Mum was distracted by a phone call or the beep of the microwave. But not today. Today she could do what she wanted. She gently tipped the plate and let the food slither into the gaping mouth of the bin.

'Don't,' said Mum. 'Please.'

'But Mummy, how can I eat when I'm so unhappy?' she stood triumphant, liberated from food for at least a day. Mum stared up at Poppy, with eyes like two dried capers: hard and bitter. 'And how do you think the rest of us feel watching you slowly kill yourself?' The bravado left Poppy as quickly as it had come.

'Everything is about you. Your bloody meal plan, your bloody exams, your bloody lies.' All the years of pent up caring spewed onto the table between them as the plate fell and rocked slowly from side to side, smears of fat pooling around the rim as it stilled. Poppy sniffed and Mum became herself again, all whimpering contrition. 'I'm so sorry,' she reached out for her daughter's hand. 'I didn't mean it.' Poppy let her hand be held in the silence that sat between them as heavy as the bags of uneaten food that had been secreted away since this all began.

'Why do you do it?' Mum's voice was kinder now, quiet in the aftermath of the explosion.

The truth was that Poppy didn't know why she did it but she did know that by not eating she felt nothing and that was infinitely better than feeling anything. 'Sometimes I just want it all to go away. Everything. Just to disappear and be gone.'

Mum laughed. Not in a nice way like when Poppy was a kid and they had chased waves at the beach, but in the way of a woman gone mad, a woman who didn't have the words to express her loss. 'You really think you have to starve yourself to disappear? Oh my darling girl,' she encircled Poppy's feeble wrists with her forefinger and thumb as if to manacle them together. 'Life will do that for you.' Fruit flies settled on the rim of the smoothie. Poppy wriggled her wrists free and rubbed the pink welts that were starting to show. 'I'm going to shower. Will you be OK?' She was surprised to find she cared. She stood in front of the bathroom mirror and peeled off the layers of clothes. Her fingers traced the outline of her body; her collar bones felt hard, which was odd because they looked spongy, and when she felt for the bulge of her belly there was only tightness and bone. She could make no sense of it; the reflection of her body was round yet the edges were sharp. In the shower she turned the temperature up until her skin turned as red as a freshly boiled lobster but no matter how hot it was it couldn't purge the feeling of disgust she had for herself. Her Mum was right; she was a selfish, ugly, fat cow. The skin on her thighs stung as the fresh cuts poached in the boiling water.

When Mum knocked on the door Poppy didn't answer, just stood once more in front of the mirror. Her reflection was misted with steam that softened the edges of her hideous body. Mum came in and Poppy didn't shout or scream for her to get out, to mind her own business. As the mist escaped through the door it was as though her mirror image stepped under a spotlight to reveal a hunched body of pink, pinched flesh. Poppy recoiled and instinctively wrapped her arms across her torso in an effort to hide from herself. Mum slowly undressed and turned the shower on but instead of stepping under the water she moved closer to Poppy and gently peeled her hands from her sheltering body. They stood side by side facing themselves, naked and silent as the steam billowed around them and kissed the mirror with an opaque mist that blurred them, obscured them, and, finally, erased them.

Ilford, July, 2008

Elif Soyler

I stood in my parents' bedroom in front of the dust-flecked
full-length mirror that was twice my height, staring
at my nose. I didn't see the way it cradled my face
as I turned my head this way and that way. I saw the width
and the curve and I traced a finger down the bridge
and across, feeling for the bones, feeling
for where the cartilage began like the slimy part of a boiled
chicken drumstick, for where the flesh could be pinched
and pulled and pushed upwards into prettier shapes
like I saw on the commercials that played
for twenty minutes at a time in between
my father's comedies from the seventies
that were never that funny.
The murky images of poor men and poor villages of mud
and manure houses and women with flirtatious fringes
and electric blue eyeshadow were stretched even further, blurred
by the forty-eight inch flat screen mounted on the wall.
He laughed and I laughed along, looking at him and not at the telly.
When Ramadan rolled around in the summer we celebrated
Eid a day early and when we drove past the school to visit
people with names I cannot remember, I saw the playground
was swarming with screaming games of hide and seek
and stuck in the mud as kids passed each other the lurgies
with a simple shove on the back and if your fingers
weren't crossed you were dirty and no one sat with you as
you ate turkey salami sandwiches at lunchtime, all the while,
thinking of Aunty stood in her long black robes by the swings
in Jubilee Park with traces of a strange man's spit wiped
from her face mingling with angry tears, the salty enzymes scorching
her skin as she clutched her son's hand and told
him not to play with a white kid's bike
without asking first.

Insanity

Liz Lane

Generation COVID. Corona. SARS-CoV-2. Ages 16 to 25. '96 to '05. Generation Locked-Up. Fucked-Up. Pissed-off. Bastards of Providence in Generation Framed. We are the scapegoats. Reckless. Fined—but what's the real cost? £40k in debt for a degree I didn't get at University Blackboard, University Zoom. University experience: stories from a room. Nine grand cost. Failed economy reigned. Tuition fees in '98 and this is what we gained? Thrust into a Britain that the Boomers have made. Brexit Britain. Boris Britain—is this what Britain became? We couldn't vote. We couldn't pick. We were dismissed with an eye roll. Extinction Rebellion was booed from the front row. Booed by the fat wrists counting at the earth pot. The ones who made its laws, bought their shit and let the world rot. The ones who didn't know to teach kids about race. Who erased black history and tried to save face. Who for ten years let the inequality grow, beggary visibly rise in the trickle-down show. See The Birdcage closed. See the distrust rise. See the uni shut. See the Grenfell fires. Generation Cancelled. Gen Predicated Grades. Sweat poems for two years and this is how they're paid? Sitting in my room, I watch the Capitol burn. Thick smoke, dead men, see Democracy's urn. We are the Generation That Will Slowly Go Mad. Told, abandon our dreams. Take the pragmatist's plan. Unemployment rises and what chance do we have? We are the Generation Terrified. Generation Have Not. Generation Tough It. Anti-guns—

This is our shot.

Millennials make sequels. Nothing new to be had. Unless we want a reboot, it's on us to make plans. Generation Doomsday. Generation Awake. Generation Locked-Up and Lying in Wait. Imperfect where you didn't know it. Fighting where you couldn't do it. Learning where you couldn't face it. Earning what you couldn't make us. We are the Generation That Will Redefine the Narrative. We transform language, ban words that you bandaged. Brands grow greener because of our demands. Celebrities apologise because we take a stance. Trump looked a fool because we bought him out on TikTok. Raised on a tragedy, joking 'cos it won't stop. London Riots, Year 7. Terrorism, Year 10. Parkland, A-Levels. Pandemic, First Year. Reared by the leaders whose rhetoric is Fear. Distrust of the media? Harking back to Nixon. Anti-intellectual. On a post-truth spectrum. Always on our phones? We will trigger this election. Generation Mobile. Generation Savvy. Get this up on Insta. That is where we'll rally. Politicised generation? Like we had a choice. You let the babies down and now the grown have a voice. Britain needs a rebrand: that mad, creative nation. Of Shakespeare, Stormzy and two Francis Bacons. Read our manifesto. Let the mad ones rise. With Poetry and Romance. Explosions of Rhyme. Howling to the beat of *How We're All Locked Up*. Pounding on the street from where the PM's shut. Drinking 'til the lockdown Babel is falling. Searching the ashes—see the nihilists crawling. Dancing to the song of the asylum days.

Fortune caves! Vibing at the lonesome rave. Just

watch when the locked-up ones go free.

Thought Fitzgerald was good? See what these 20s will be.

Watch when the shut-up kids go astray.

Thought the Beats were good? We run towards, not away.

Indoor schemes. Generation Creation.

All that you destroyed and we're here in the making.

Generation COVID. Generation Had.

When the pandemic ends, this generation will go **mad.**

Loveless language
Beth Lane

Yes, I can hear the sweet sound of my lover's voice, and how it is as smooth as a lulling lake at dawn, or as shrill as a whistling kettle. Yet, in this world I have built around her, my love language is the way I see her. I can see the shining smile stretch sprightly across her round face, in a far brighter way than most; I can spot the subtlest misting of her eyes as the first lone tear springs. From simply the minutest furrow of her fine brows I can see the quickening drumming of irritation in her veins. I can count the freckles across her skin, white as fresh milk, witness the satisfaction when she arches her back like a cat, see the crinkles deepen beside those blinding baby blue eyes. I can read her easier than her own mother can; I can read her as if I am staring at my own familiar hands. She is all I see. Yes, I may indulge in the sound of her lyrical laughter, and my name falling from her lovely lips, but I have spent most of the seconds of every day mesmerising every dip in her creamy skin, every wrinkle across her sweet face, every grimace, every grin, every gesture. With this vibrant vision of mine, her body language is my love language.

I can see her rosy lips, cherry red against her skin, and I can see them coil downwards. It is only brief—so brief, most would miss it; yet, I can see it. I can see her morose mouth, even if she tries to mask it, twitching in distaste as I gaze blankly into our fridge's vacant space and, at first, I think it's the fridge she finds so sour, but of course, I can then see it's not. It's me. Later, as I watch the skinny arm of the second hand judder around the clock, I can see her in the distance, slouching against the staircase, and her phone illuminates the soppy slant of her mouth, a smile that is usually reserved for me alone; I can see its tenderness. I scramble through my own messages, urgently searching for when I last texted her. It was hours ago. She had read it hours ago. Upon calling her over, I can see that very doting grin drop in an instant, and I can see, as she plonks herself down beside me, the little inches she has left between us, a space that has never been there before.

As the midnight sky greets us, she runs her slender fingers through the tangled threads of my hair, and I can see her above me. I can see that her mind is faraway, longing for some other place, and I can see that her unfocused eyes never meet mine. For the entire night. Even if I do not lay my heavy head on her chest tonight, even if I do not press my ear there and hear her heart, I can see from her indifferent face that it does not beat twice as fast like mine does. And as she hides those baby blues, I can see she doesn't dream of now, us; she doesn't dream of me. I trace our ceiling's pattern in the dark for hours upon hours, with just the warmth of her body and—oh. There is a crack in the ceiling. It is ever so slight, but I can see it. I wonder if it will grow. I consider waking her, but I can see she is in a serene slumber, all the stress has slipped from her strained shoulders. It is almost perfect for a while then, because she doesn't express a thing aside from peacefulness. Her jaw hangs, drool dribbles out, and I can hear her soft snore. But then, she grins gently, and her mouth moves, forms a single syllable word. It is too quiet, so I can't hear it properly, but I don't need to. I can see it is a name. I can see that the name spoken is not mine.

I don't need to hear her say it; I have already seen it. I have already seen she is no longer in love with me. I don't need to hear her say it.

MARIA
Kyle Wakefield

When the voices downstairs make me flinch again, Maria leads me to the bed and starts to wrap me in blankets, one after the other, until the sharp edges of me are soft enough to hug. "Come on, now," she says, stroking my hair down over my eyes. "Don't panic. Nobody will believe them. After a couple more days, they won't even believe themselves. You have memories as insane as theirs too, don't you? From before you knew?"

Stiffly, the world around me muffled, I nod.

"Insane enough to make you realise beyond any doubt that I wasn't human?"

"Yeah."

Maria lays me down and smiles against my cheek. "So why didn't you? Why didn't you raise a pitchfork-wielding mob?"

She kisses my eyelids one by one. A blissful shudder goes down my back. Because I loved you, I could say. Because I believed it was a dream. I stay silent.

My memories of Maria are worse than anything our housemates said they saw. The night she ran all the way to Newcastle, a hundred and fifty miles in seven hours, because I drunkenly boarded a train instead of going home. The morning I found her in her room with her face covered in blood, not streaming from her nose or mouth but just sitting there, smeared. She didn't explain it. She was standing at her easel, and could have told me it was paint, but instead, she smiled and told me it was nothing. A brush of her hand across my cheek hypnotised my doubt away. I have found out, because of her, that the brain's desperation to find a rational explanation grows stronger when the madness does.

If there is one memory that stands out, it is the night I was kidnapped. That was the summer after we met, when I'd just started to notice her fussing me a little more in my drunkenness than Sam or Greg. I'd often wake up in my bed with the blankets tucked around me after thinking I'd settled down to sleep on the docks or the cliffs, tens of miles from our house, freezing cold and all alone. I would think she shouldn't have been able to carry me, her being a tiny girl and me a six-foot-four hulk of heavy limbs, all the heavier for being plastered.

Before I was kidnapped, I had no idea I was being followed. I have vague memories of leaving a garden party with two tequila bottles clutched in my hands the way you'd clutch daggers, wandering down wide, unfamiliar residential streets with my head craned skywards. It was a hot, stuffy night, the clouds low and swollen like steam. I guess the three men in the white car assessed that even though I was tall for a man, even taller for a woman—whichever of the two they decided I was—I was too floppy to put up a fight, so they idled beside me for a moment and pulled me into the back seat by my long hair.

I don't think I said anything. I was forced upright in the middle, between four grabbing hands, hands that took my leather trench coat and my wallet and my phone and my boots and my watch and started pawing at my gold blouse before one of them found the Primark label. I remember watching intently, my head pulled back by a hand still snarled in my hair, as they turned the boots over and said Come on, man, come on, this goth punk shit's worth hundreds of quid, the buckles alone would cost you your mum, and I suppose they figured out they were right, because they stuffed it all into the footwells and drove on. I started nodding and two arms came across my chest in an X shape. They couldn't get my seatbelt around me. I was sitting on it.

Panic wasn't where it should have been. Panic was outside the dark-tinted windows, crackling past like the wind. Panic was sitting on my chest, crushing my lungs, but I couldn't take it into my mouth and taste the flavour of it and fill my stomach with it because that hand was still in my hair, pulling my head flush back. I could think, yes. I thought about being beaten up and maybe murdered and maybe chained up in Buffalo Bill's red-brick dungeon, having my teeth pulled out for jewellery and my swollen drunk mouth stuffed with moths. But that's all I did. I thought.

The car left Aberdeen, taking me at breathtaking speed towards the dark of the hills. Like he could read my mind, one of them asked something about death, about whether I wanted to die, and when I started laughing, he punched me in the face.

That's what it was all about, I suppose. All the drunken wandering, lying down to sleep in the most magnificently freezing places I could find, places I thought my friends couldn't reach. I was trying to get myself killed, in a way that would make me look blameless.

As the car plunged deeper into the countryside, I found out to my dismay that they planned to dump me out in the nearest village. Alive. All they wanted was my money and my clothes. I suppose they were hoping I would wade my way back to Aberdeen, alone, cold, and lose my memory before I found the police.

While we were still in the dark, though, the man who'd punched me in the face said something to the driver, who said something back to him, and then all three of them turned to look out of the back window. There was someone following us, they said. She'd been following since Aberdeen. A little lass on a motorbike.

I swooned after that. When I woke up, I was rolling over and over and over on the road, my mouth throbbing with pain where I'd struck it. The car was speeding away, arms scrabbling to close the back door. I came to a stop and spat out a long string of vomit and blood and thought I saw my tooth in it.

Then, something shot past me. It wasn't a motorbike. It was too silent and too fast, and when it caught up with the white car, the white car folded in half like a fortune cookie and reared up onto its front wheels. There was an enormous crash, a manufactured whining sound like someone tearing open a rusty gate, a vibration through the tarmac that made my lungs shake and my hair fly up like it was weightless. I swooned again, I think, and when my eyes listed open, the whole world was green like an American storm-season sky, the moon huge and far too close to the ground, haemorrhaging white light in sprays. After an age of dry blinking, I saw it wasn't the moon. A pylon had come down across the road. It was not quite lying, but leaning, the wires holding its spark-vomiting head just out of the dirt. Beyond it were the golden lights of a village, picked out like little campfires on the black hill.

I remember thinking, half-conscious and high on the half-melted stink of petrol and tarmac, that it couldn't be right. The car hadn't hit a pylon. It had hit something in the middle of the road, something that ran past me at breakneck speed to reach it. It hit the pylon afterwards. The shadow flung it sideways.

"Scotty," someone said in the distance.

I realised I was sitting up. I was sitting up on the road with my socked feet in a puddle, the wind ravishing my bare arms, and my back against Maria's motorbike, the engine deliciously hot on the back of my neck.

Maria staggered up to me, covered in blood, her hair red with it. There was blood dribbling out of her mouth and when she said my name again, her voice was soft and swollen, like she was missing teeth. She was holding her stomach hard, her whole body bent around it.

She wasn't coming to me from the bike. She was coming to me from the tangled wreck of pylon and car. One of the men was lying next to the car, dark and formless and edge-lit like a puddle. I didn't think he had fallen or crawled or been flung. I thought I had seen the black shadow staggering to the back door and dragging him out by his lapels and doing something to him, something that fastened her head tight to his throat and made her contort backward in ecstasy, lifting his struggling body high into the air. I thought he was lying there because that was where Maria had thrown the flattened shell of him down in a huff, soul sucked out.

"C'mon," Maria slurred, and picked me up like I weighed nothing. I was too drunk to sit up in her arms and so much taller than her that my feet and hands touched the road on either side. I couldn't speak, my mouth stretched rubbery and loose by the toothache.

She got onto the bike and lolled me against her, wrapping my arms around her waist. She held them there herself, still compressing her middle with one hand as she drove. I fell asleep, one eye-socket mashed into the bones at the back of her neck.

The next morning, I woke up in my bed with all my teeth intact and both feet dry. There was a blanket tucked tight around me and my coat, boots, wallet and phone were laid out with Maria's finicky neatness on the desk beneath the window. None of it was bloody. None of it was scorched. None of it stank of petrol or smoke.

I left my room believing it all. I believed she'd brought me home on her motorbike. I believed she'd tailgated the car for twenty miles until the kidnappers threw me out in a panic. I believed that she'd gotten off the bike to prop me up and stepped in front of the speeding car and that the car had imploded when it touched her like she was made of solid steel and rooted a hundred feet into the ground. I believed the blood she'd come to me covered in wasn't hers. For the inexcusable crime of hurting me, she'd eaten my attackers alive. Then, I saw her in the light of day, playing snakes and ladders with Sam and Greg in the kitchen in her fluffy dressing-gown with tousled hair and sleepy eyes, and decided, systematically and deliberately, to believe it no more.

That was the moment I first loved her, I think. The moment I saw her for real after another ultraviolent-indie-film night and saw no trace of that version of her left. I didn't fall in love with vengeful, vicious Maria, the guardian angel sent from red-drunk Heaven to save my life over and over again with fire and blood and moonlight blazing in her hair; I fell in love with the ordinary one. The friend who did her human best and no more. The one who couldn't help me.

"My darling," she says, as I start to sob in her arms. "Don't be frightened. They won't ever know what we are. I promise."

She spends a lot of these nights, these nights in my airless room with Sam and Greg making noise in the house beneath us and my body trussed in blankets, begging to know how long I've been in love with her. I can't tell her what made me realise. I can't tell her I fell in love with her only after I'd convinced myself that all those memories were dreams. I can't tell her the real reason why I'm crying. I'm not terrified our housemates will find out what we are. Not anymore. She could take care of them, as she takes care of the others. I'm terrified that one day, once the knowledge that it's all true has sunk into my bones, I will stop loving her and love that blazing demon instead.

Maybe Tomorrow (Collection)
Olliver Gillo

Hanwells 18
Touch the doors of Hanwells, feel the surface of needles and white powder and sugar,
And consider walking in to a temple of feverish delusions.
Push against the hermetic gates and let gravity suck you in and enjoy
Wheezing through the green sickly air, thick with plastics and cloying solvents.
Peruse the shelves, stuffed end to end, with landfill-primed articles for purchase.
Ogle at the scrap fit for braking, let silicon breasts lure you in,
And in the next isle.
Gaunt waxy children hunched over mould presses, sweating in stifling basement passages
Oriental wise elders trembling, eye to eye with furious Pacific tantrums
All the world straining like a diseased heart, groaning with our unrelenting industry
Whilst the 'coloured' people suffer why should you bother?
The heady thump of halogen bleaches with its gleam,
Away from the desert seas and jungle scenes, we don't have to hear them scream.
But dare to pick up this or that, feel in your palm that cheap rubber tat
And you'll be complicit in this act.
At the checkout the 'biddy' takes her time, fingering the coppers, and chatting, she's kind.
You eye up the assistant, watch them reach for the moon.
Thanks for shopping at Hanwells, we hope to see you soon.

Snap-shot 7
I remember the tragic prosopon
Painted on the boy with the clothes on,
Behind
She screams in her delicate form.
Wan in terror,
Trangbang
Vietnam.

Can't un-play 10
I remember waking up from childhood with a lifeless figure in my hands.
I cradled him dearly and tried to whisper an alternate end through my tears.
The curtain had unveiled, the illusion was up. Death is final, miserable. Unplanned
And caught off-guard, the drawbridge lowered, the box opened, attacked by fears,
I sat orphaned of naivety and ignorance; My virgin thoughts raped of their innocence.
Flavours of war turned bitter in my mouth, as Mothers lay crying
Fevered victims reached out to me, deformed and straining,
Disease left them vulnerably misshapen like in paintings. I
couldn't continue as a child thereafter, not once I understood that
Death means dying.

In the box 37
Inhale… exhale…
Sweat. Wet down my face.
Vacuum packed abs.
Hammer'd heart tender.
Curls and swerves, bestial grace.
The glutinous pigs peer, lips licking.
Beady eyes unblinking.
SWOOSH
I drop like an Iraq veteran
The calisthenic of his form;
Unfurling, graceful.
I smell blood.
Punch, PUNCH.
I push him to the rope.
Crunch crunch, they stuff their mouths.
Electric skin.
Uppercut.
Violent pupils, swollen veins,
Pumping rage. Mutt out of luck.
Animal.
Apes in a cage.
The mallet whips, rings out across the hall, deer locking horns.
I seethe savagely with shaking fists
Hatred
An Amaryllis drowns in bubbling petrol,
Waves thunder as they hurtle.
The belt is poised, scorpion sting,
Bearded monster. We lock shoulders.
The whip—crack—blood—scream,
Arms aching.
Skin on skin.
My knuckles find his face.
Nose to nose, framed in pain.
White fear stares back at me.
Hot breath, panting like bulls,
Like lovers.
Inhale… exhale…

Memories
Ruby Skippings

Can you feel the sparks shooting round your skull? Shapes coldly press against exposed skin, forcing you back where you didn't ask to be. Left alone under a bunkbed, trying to inhale without rippling the air. Ribcage compressed beneath the weak wood and yet secure in the cocoon of being unseen. Creaking doors and speckling dust dancing in sun beams. Loud screams clash against window panes, fantasy play you escaped with. Rolling hills and happy endings emerging from solitude. Tattered books and taps dripping in sync, like words written to be read with firm rhythm. They are kept in time by eternal fate. Itching against fabric on filthy bus decks, thrown against the bars as you watch two women leave a fluorescent nail sign behind and think at any other second, you wouldn't have watched their mouths extend and purse, their fingers intertwine. Sick trees drop leaves and pines, piercing school bells bring waves of nausea. You chew off acid nail-polish and pull fabric down over blossoming bruises. He promised you a big bite that day. He drank your ruby blood. Bared teeth, bitter lemon curd, embarrassment flushing at your ears, all by the time the mid-day heat has arrived. You could feel it in your core. Pavement cracks under your feet as wisps of car fumes and previous plane paths mingle with the midnight hues. Stars reflecting out to one another, like ticking sand in an hourglass, a forgotten childhood inescapably coming back in a fever dream.

Boudica

Ruby Skippings

In the end, the rule is to not cross me.
The crimes against my husband
His gentile nature prime for defaming
And naturally, you assumed I was the same,
I was prepared to be shamed
I would sit idly by and watch the ruin of my name
But what you failed to see is the burning rage—
The fire you did not intend to ignite
When you stole from us our dignity
Honour, lacking from your vocabulary,
Boiled in my blood and spread like an infection
Epidemic across Iceni, the Queen who'll never be
Recruited more than they could forsee
Rebels like me, they needed a leader
A figurehead, someone with the passion of the
Chief's corpse on her shoulders, perhaps,
Seeing red, red, 100,000 dead and more to come
We will storm through your capital, your province, your
Heart, heart on my plate, heart in my hands
After all, massacres tend to communicate
What a devastated legacy cannot
So that's the route I took. Beast of the belly and no turning back
My daughters, flogged and raped, I will take your innocence too
I will take your empire, I will take
It all. Darkness creeps in, eternal doomsday
Bittersweet juice upon my lips, I
Rest my head for the first time in centuries
The screams ring out, you think this can be feigned
But I conquered you. The scars remain.

monochrome

Dylan Davies

your suits were how i knew i was third in line.
you sent old videos, your shaking hands ripping photos
of your first girlfriend, you in your red co-ord.

as friends, i first entered your flat to pick up
my club heels; i saw your orange gowns lean
pinstripe first from your broken wardrobe door.

with me, you wore yellow. i loved when you sat
amongst flowers. they seemed to turn their faces
towards you when you moved, as i did.

we felt at home in yellow, stayed there awhile.
you told me, fingers looped around my fourth finger,
you hoped you would have the pleasure of stopping

there. i saw you on the tube. monochrome pantsuit,
sapphire blue, blazer and all, right down to the shoe.
you didn't see me but i saw you,

and your suit—it was green after me
but now it has moved. you've found a new colour.
i'm happy for you.

My Sister

Badriya Abdullah

Small babe,
Spring arrived in my arms
And you charmed your way into my heart.
Nature pledged to shelter you,
As I had promised to,
And the trees bowed before their new ward.
Small babe, you bloomed.
We spoke in a tongue only we understood,
I heard your cries in a way mama never could.
You fell, you tumbled, you grew, you stumbled
You fumbled for my hand,
And I promised I would never leave you.

Even as you grew too large
For my arms to shield you
From the brambles of Summer.
The pricks of thorns
Soon appeared on your fingertips.
Small babe, you changed.
Pain didn't scare you as it scared me
Warm red sap from ebony branches
Caught your eye.
You learned that reward demands sacrifice
And laughed defiantly in Summer's face
As you held its beauty in your hands.
The apple beckoned you higher up the tree.
You climbed further than I could follow.
You let me watch you fall.

Strong child,
Autumn came.
You fell, you bled,
You pushed me away as I yelled your name,
You learned what I had always known:
The scars on my fingers came from the flowers,
The scrapes on my knees came from the trees,
And no one is sheltered by nature forever,
I had to let you go.

The winds of Winter tell me

You've created shelter.
I hope they tell you I've done the same.
I whisper your name to the trees,
They remember, faintly.
Small babe, strong child, sister of mine,
Stronger than I ever knew.

My sky is not blue

Emma Bullen

It used to be cream with a skirting board
pinched at the edge
and strands of sticky tape forgotten
from old Christmas decorations.

The tinsel would hang in smiles
around the edge until I decided
to cling to those grins,
but the tape ripped off the paint
and tinsel wilted beside my broken arm.

Almond Cream No. 620
A matt cream base with warm undertones
was bleached by the energy efficient bulbs
my mum would buy
that washed the living room
into an overexposed photo.
It made my friends wince,
and I started complaining of headaches.

We had a problem with damp
that ate into the corners
I used to think it was a spider's nest
until it morphed into a menacing face
mottled with black eyes and teeth
that fed on cream paint and white light.
My dad would buy
Dettol Mould and Mildew Remover
and the mouldy monster faded into coffee stains.

Now I look up at my sky
the bits of sticky tape have rotated
as I am not allowed to stand on chairs,
and the bulbs have been replaced with
Warm White Energy Savers.
The damp worsens each year
as the stains become espresso
but the chemicals my dad uses
are always the same.
My sky is not blue

it is cream with chipped
paint and black spots,
the sticky tape is laughing at me
and the stained corners are closing in.
Now before me is an empty room

and my sky is no longer mine.

Not Me

Oihane Garcia

A moony, realist tone heaping in your throat
and you gulping down. Your plans happened to be
rotten splinters. The obstinate look in your eyes
is gone, but I can still catch
a furtive glimpse of clairvoyance
stirring your insides
when I let you hold my palms.
You don't try to involve me, or force me,
in your life anymore. You don't square
your smile between sly dimples
or tug blighted words behind my ear.
There's no more ear left for you
to bite, to chew, to spit out.
The attempt to convert me
into post-impressionism
has now become stale.
No rosemary and no roses.
You dare not foist any on me, you dare not
call for anything in return.
A bath of luna and siesta
to spoil my wounds; reading
'Blood Wedding' out loud
was not enough.
I did not want to be your blade of grass.

      But now you listen,
and in the cacophony of the kitchen
the radio yields:

When the cat gut binds my ankles to your bedstead/
That ain't love, no that ain't love.

Bonheur de Vivre, by Henri Matisse

Oihane Garcia

In Collioure the sun hides inside
a stained glass colour lamp and
radiates a fierce, fauvist expression of
mediterranean 'still life'.
The complicit sea lets a climax of luminosity
tint the sinuous lines of bodies pink, as the
heat of midday's clear sky reflects a brighter
yellow on the already golden sand.
If Pyramus and Thisbe had made it,
they'd probably incarnate the lovers
in the corner: Twisting tongues in an earthly kiss
to the beat of a voyeur shepherd's song.
Naked Majas blatantly stare at each other
with their irises soaked in aquamarine and light green.
 Then, the foliage transitions to orange;
and everyone but the indecisive clarinetist
finds harmony in fallen arms, as fallen leaves.

      About freedom (and mischief),
the French were never wrong.
And in this parenthesis of closed museums,
I wonder how many people dream
of Sardana dances, hoping to wake up
exhausted, someday, when life resumes,
in an Arcadian scene.

At the antique shop

Oihane Garcia

Would you believe antique lovers
always gloss over technical problems?

'See, dear, I knew a young man once.
He ignored
the ticking's extinguishing rhythm,
yet he dusted
his collector's edition clock
with the same religious devotion
believers slip their fingers through
old, priceless, rosary beads.
Yes, closing down
still reminds me of him,
communing at ungodly hours
before ill-fated clock hands.
It took him a long time,
you know, to realise the resented
click in the rusted gearbox
would not ever
bless him anew.

Observed as a Guest

Charlotte Cassidy

Tom couldn't remember the last time that he had left the family cottage, a house hidden on a narrow lane. He had become accustomed to the silence, accepting its place as if it were a black cat that had woken up outstretched on his duvet one morning. For a while, this cat made Tom believe that he had company. But this companionship was brief and, even though it never left Tom's house, it soon slunk back to the shadows.

Tom smiled as he felt Abigail's hands wrapping around his waist. Turning the tap on, he watched the kitchen sink start to fill with water before looking out of the window. His eyes were too tired to take in the vibrant colours of the back garden. Abigail had arrived at dawn without notice but with her forgiveness and, for the first time in years, Tom felt content.

"It hasn't changed a bit." Abigail's voice tickled Tom's neck.

"What hasn't?" Tom asked.

"The garden."

A plate slipped from Tom's hands; it did not crack in the shallow water, but he still flinched. "It's messier than before," he chuckled.

"Well, the elderflower tree looks the same. It still blooms beautifully."

"The petals are beginning to fall."

"It's always a bit sad after that happens, isn't it?"

Tom turned his head to look at her. "It's just a tree. It'll bloom again."

"You haven't changed either." Abigail frowned. "You've barely aged."

Tom kissed the top of Abigail's head. "I've missed you."

"I've missed you too, and this house. Lucille seems to love it."

Tom rolled his shoulders back, looking at Lucille lying in the garden. Her hands were pressed over her eyes to protect them from the sun and her shoulders had begun to shine red. He lowered his eyes back down as he poured a half-empty mug of tea into the sink, browning the bubbles.

"I'm sorry you've been on your own for so long but it's going to be perfect now," Abigail said. "Now that we're back together again."

"And you're here to stay with me forever, right?" Tom asked.

Abigail touched his cheek with a cold hand before she kissed him. "Come on, we should go join Lucille in the garden. You and I can lie under the elderflower tree like we used to."

"I don't really go into the garden," Tom answered.

"You should speak to Lucille, she's so sweet—she didn't have a lot of friends at university but that's only because she's shy. Besides, she's a graduate now, so you have that in common. I know you two will get along and it'll be nice for her to have some company this summer...so come outside with me?" Abigail wrapped her arms around his neck.

Tom shook his head and pulled her arms off him. "It's okay, I'll keep my distance."

"Why?"

Tom failed to reply and Abigail eventually left him standing by the sink. He squinted at the steamy window, where the colours of the garden were now distorted. Abigail went out to the garden. She remembered how she had spent an evening after school with Tom making elderflower cordial from the tree by the back gate. They drank it diluted with gin over several evenings; she and Tom would lie out on the grass with pleasantly heavy limbs, talking about how summer would be the perfect time for a wedding.

She sat down beside Lucille, who smelt of sun cream and aloe vera. Her hair was shining, as if she were reflecting gold back to the sun and, under her breath, she was singing a song about a house that used to belong to somebody.

"Tom says 'hi'," Abigail said, "He would have come out to join us, but he has an unhealthy obsession with staying pale."

Lucille had stopped singing. She sat up and smiled at Abigail, her eyes finding comfort in the familiarity. Abigail hated conversations that consisted of only a few words, and Lucille had never been one to talk about anything that could go unsaid.

"I'm so excited that you're staying with us!" Abigail grinned. "Tom's house truly is beautiful. His father left it to him when Tom was sixteen to go travelling through Africa…or Asia. I thought that Tom would have sold it by now, especially after I left him alone here. It's good that he didn't. And it's good that we're here. This garden has been the only place where I've wanted to be, even after all this time."

"Should hire a gardener," Lucille said sadly.

"Yeah, I don't know why Tom hasn't done anything." Abigail frowned before pulling a blade of grass from the ground, slowly so she could feel the root slipping away from the soil.

Lucille lowered herself back to the grass and Abigail followed her like a shadow. Lucille began to hum her tune; it sounded like a lullaby from years gone by. It reminded Abigail of Tom, so she turned to face the back door, feeling the lawn tickling her cheek.

The Tom in her mind was different, tanned with shoulder-length hair like he used to have at twenty-one. All her memories of him were old, like sepia photographs with fading edges. She tried to picture how things would be now; she contemplated that until the elderflower tree's shadow covered her completely.

Evening faded into night like a dying match. Tom had just cleared the plates from dinner. Lucille had not joined them; she was still in the garden. He sat down on the familiar seats, which were too tall for the dining table, and looked at Abigail opposite him. Tom watched her red-stained lips as she spoke, before his eyes moved to her glass swishing wine dangerously close to the brim.

"She's still in a sundress. How is she not cold?" Abigail asked, turning to face the window while stretching the sleeves of her green cardigan over her fingers. "I'm freezing."

"I lit a fire," Tom murmured. He thought Abigail would have noticed it, seeing as the only other light in the room was the pendant lamp hanging from a low beam.

"Oh…I can't feel it." Abigail shrugged.

The door creaked open and, from out of the sharp shadows, Lucille stepped into sight. For a time, she stood there looking around the room, like a visitor in a museum wondering which artefact to study first. Eventually, she edged to the bookshelf that stood behind Abigail, the one that Tom had built to structure his empty days. She picked up one of the many hardbacks; Tom had not read any of them for years as he did not want to disturb the frail pages. A thick layer of dust had settled on their spines and Lucille stroked one before blowing her finger as if it were a dandelion. Tom rolled his shoulders as she shoved the book back on the shelf only to grab another.

Holding his glass to his mouth, Tom allowed the aged wine to touch his lips without taking a sip. His nose began to fog the glass' edge as he glared at Lucille. She walked away from the bookshelf, hardback in her hand. Tom drained the rest of his wine before grabbing the bottle.

"It's good wine. I didn't know you had seventeen-year-old wine, Tom," Abigail remarked, tilting her head to read the date on the label. She was no longer wearing her cardigan. Her eyes followed Lucille to the window. "It's so strange how fast the days seem to go, isn't it, Lucille? It feels like you and I only got here yesterday."

"You arrived at dawn today," Tom answered.

"I just feel like I never get to see enough of the sun, don't you agree?" Abigail hurried to the window to join Lucille and looked outside at the shadows frolicking in the moonlight.

Lucille sat down on the window seat, opening a thin book draped in a blue dust jacket as an elderflower stem slipped out onto the floor. She let its paper slide in between her fingers as she flicked through the yellowed pages. Abigail sat down next to Lucille, resting her chin on her shoulder to catch only glimpses of words and pictures in the dim light.

A glossy photo print slid out from the book as Lucille flicked the page; it was of Abigail and Tom on their last day of school. Abigail looked at the photograph over Lucille's shoulder. She could not remember who took the picture, but she did recall how a couple of Tom's friends had yanked his tie so tightly that their English teacher had to cut it off with a pair of blunt scissors. She could faintly see the friction burns on his neck.

But Tom was smiling in the polaroid, not caring about how sore his neck must have felt. He refused to put the tie back on and had left his shirt collar unbuttoned. It was strange seeing him so nonchalant standing in the sun with his school years behind him. Abigail was beaming next to him, not knowing that she would be crying in his garden a few hours later.

Abigail looked at Tom while he was refilling his glass with wine. Their eyes met. She heard Lucille slipping the photograph back into the book. Abigail turned to Lucille before stroking her hair, letting the curls slip in between her fingers. Lucille leant back and Abigail kissed the top of her head.

A clang suddenly filled the room and Abigail felt Lucille flinch. A glass was on the floor next to Tom and his arm was hanging limply off the chair. He was glaring at the back door, which was still ajar, before looking at Abigail. With an exaggerated sigh, she stood up and felt the crunch of elderflower from underneath her foot. She closed the door with a bang, making Lucille recoil again.

Tom's face relaxed as Abigail walked to the table, his mouth opening to say something before closing it with a swallow. She picked up the glass.

"It's okay, Lucille," she said. "It didn't break."

"Do you want any more wine?" Tom asked loudly, dragging the bottle across the wooden table. He frowned before tipping it upside down. Only a few drops leaked out.

"You didn't offer Lucille any," Abigail said pointedly, making Tom shrug.

"I'm fine," Lucille softly announced, joining them at the table.

"You drank it all, Tom!"

"It's okay. I'm fine," Lucille repeated. She stepped up onto one of the empty chairs and then to the table, her eyes transfixed on the beam.

"She needs to get down, Abs," Tom said through gritted teeth, glaring at Lucille as she disappeared into the shadows above the pendant lamp.

"She's just exploring, Tom," Abigail defended.

"She's not allowed up there."

"Why are you being so sensitive?"

"She's disrupting everything."

"Lucille's allowed to be curious, Tom."

"Not about this room."

"Why?"

Tom groaned, rubbing his neck as he stood up. "Come on, let's go to bed."

Abigail shook her head, looking up at Lucille's looming form in the dark. "I'm not going to leave her alone in the room like this."

"Fine. Stay with her then." Tom sighed before leaving the room.

Abigail stared at the door that Tom had just slammed until the echo faded. All she could hear was Lucille's heavy breathing and the table creaking under her feet. Hesitantly, Abigail joined her, almost hitting her head on the low-hanging beam on the way up. Lucille was tracing her fingers over the beam and Abigail did the same. The wood was rough, with shards of black paint peeling away under their fingertips. Looking at Lucille, she thought that she would understand why they were up here. But Lucille's face had become vacant and, she stared into the darkness with her arms wrapped around the beam like ivy.

Of Age

Eleanor Davies

As I walked the weeks towards eighteen
I stopped making my mother happy
by dancing or brushing my teeth.
Small limbs loafing on kitchen floor
she saw me wrapped in golden foil.
Suddenly she touched my cheek
to pull me from hormonal cement
and I remembered being fizzy and young,
small and wire-headed, bright, fresh-skinned,
she smiled at her girl through lunch time.
Now we feel sick to sit here,
a table and a lifetime between
any love she has and my pale 18 year old body.
A woman.
I live in her house.
She wakes me up on weekdays.

Open Letter to the Ministry of Exorcisms—(Sestina)

Seb Gale

I have never felt the cataloguing of ghosts
to be one of the more necessary aspects
of modern bureaucracy, for ghosts will wait in lines
all the same, tickling the promise of doors
and stables which creak at night
with all the weight of their intents.
A noting of intents
would give more deference to these ghosts,
because each of them reference the night
as companion to their ghoulish—or gormless—aspects,
but very few would espouse the astral doors
to come out with such lines
as 'FEAR ME! Scatter your hopes in rotten lines
before my scythe! Forsake all intents
of love and passion—' and so on. The doors
will mostly open for relatively friendly ghosts
who, like you and me, are uninterested in most aspects
of modern politics, find Saturday Night
a bore, and 'Saturday Night
Live' one of the less inclusive title lines.
Why, after all, should my long-dead grandmother miss such seminal aspects
of Andy Samberg's career? She may not be live, but for all intents
and purposes might enjoy another G & T after the ghosts
of Presley, Muddy, Jimi, and the Doors
have shut up shop and closed doors
on the twilight-zone's sell-out show, 'Yesterday Night
at the London Palladium.' And she said some ghosts
have been queuing for half a century, doing lines
around the dreamtime, looping Top Ghoul twice while your intents
are directed to the study of ectoplasm? I don't find these aspects
of government funding the most relevant aspects,
not when some poor soul's visitation is denied, and the doors
are closed to him; spectre-come-thumb-twiddler, milking his intents
and aspirations—because ghosts have them too—into the night.
To conclude frankly, you forget there can be passion in ghosts.
So tomorrow night when I write on the dotted lines
that my intents are harmless, account for this and open the doors;
I want to relive the ghosts of an old love, and watch her sleep, heavenly in aspects.

No Questions, Tongue No. 44

Seb Gale

'If I ask you to turn
your tongue out with your pockets,
then I'd expect a smile's criminal courtesy.
Pay me with your words, won't you? Because I'm not
a sock to be fucked but I'm not a picture in a locket, love; I'm the
blue translucent gargoyle, or the Harry Hill fanatic laced up to chinstraps
and waiting – of course —for my tongue to get crucified, mummified or calcified at the least.
'Give me your tongue,' he says, 'because a dissident head is a pipe-bomb and you can't
say that word in the queue, and a dissident heart is an apple that fits the heel of
nobody's boots. Pretend like they taught you and hobble on, won't you? Don't make me
take a minute to consider the road to Damascus; that A1 dustbowl with no service, that
roadside café with meal deals unholy; the Holy Holy rubble and—who the fuck wants
cheese and onion anyway? I never got there before—turned back at Michael's throbbing sword and
I wouldn't make the trip again. So yeah. Turn your tongue out with your pockets?'
        I look this man up and down,
and wonder about his homelife.

Sacro Monte Haikus

Seb Gale

I

Wax faces like prongs
to prod spiritual loins.
A strange smell in here.

II

I didn't trust her,
the Mary from Varallo.
No eye contact made.

III

Tripped over in the
fifth room of Revelations.
A badly placed lamb.

Pregnancy test
Sadie Harte

wrap up the morning's despair
and I see your ghost

I can't get the want
for a positive out of me

for you to suffocate me
how you do when you fall

across my spinal skin
and crush my lungs with love

don't you know I'd kill
for the suffocation

for the mauve mornings
of being alive

just being yours
nothing more

in the village of cherry blossoms

softly, pneumonia from the bathtub,
kissed me, vermilion from the violence.

Words for when you swallowed me whole

Sadie Harte

half laid on all soul's day
with Narcissian death in your mouth.
I drank the blood sweet and dark,
curled down into your stomach;
a landing pad for smoke and dinner.
you let teardrops salt your mouth,
guided the crying to my resting place;
chin tilted for melancholy's drink.
I'm in love with the hallelujah,
with what had been our echo chamber.

Saturday Morning

Ersi Zevgoli

EXT. AIDAN'S PARENTS HOUSE—MORNING
A street in Norwich, in the Golden Triangle. Two-storey brick houses closely together. AIDAN and STEPH, both in their early forties, stand on the street, looking in on a door with stained glass detailing (a small, but well-kept house in all), shoulder to shoulder, looking up at the top window. Aidan sighs, as if going to battle. Steph lets his head drop on Aidan's shoulder. They are in jeans, jumpers, jackets, and scarves. It is overcast, and the light is crisp and cold, like the end of autumn or the beginning of winter.

STEPH: You'll be fine. If it gets too much... Give me a call.

AIDAN: I'm not ready.

STEPH: (hugging Aidan's hand affectionately) I know, I know... Do you want me to come with you?

AIDAN: (rousing himself) No, no. I'm just being silly. It'll be fine.

STEPH: (throwing a rueful sideways glance at Aidan) And I doubt I'll be welcome, after last time they came round...

AIDAN: (smiling a little) What was it that you said? After you told her that, you know, she is always out to get me.

STEPH: (very seriously and innocently)
That she should sometimes just shut the fuck up and give you a break.
They look at each other, and a giggle escapes them.

AIDAN: Verbatim.

STEPH: I have an excellent memory. That was a direct quote.

They laugh for a moment longer, but Aidan's attention turns back to the front of the house. His mirth disappears, and a tired, sad look returns on his face. Steph squeezes his arm, as he looks at Aidan with concern. Aidan nods, sniffles a little, and walks up the tiny path to the front door. Steph stands still, and as Aidan reaches the front door, he turns to look at him. Steph smiles in encouragement.

STEPH: I'll be at the Nero round the corner.
He nods, waves, and Steph starts walking slowly to the end of the street. Aidan takes a deep breath, and knocks on the door.

                    INT. AIDAN'S PARENTS' HOUSE—HALLWAY—MORNING
The hallway of Aidan's parents' house on the inside. The front door is in the centre of the frame. The house feels cold, even a little severe—cool toned light filters in through the windows. Everything is in order, tidied up, the colour scheme is cool toned, only the wellies standing by the door seem to be dirty.

AIDAN'S MUM enters the frame, and answers the door. She is a short, elegant woman in her 70s, with dyed brown hair.

MUM: Where've you been? You said you'd be here at half ten.

AIDAN: And good morning to you too, lovely to see you. Aidan's mum presents her cheek, and Aidan kisses it, but she doesn't return the kiss. She steps aside, lets him in, and shuts the door behind him. She walks out of frame the same way she came in. Aidan is left alone for a moment on screen, looking exhausted already.

MUM (O.S.): Coffee?

Aidan follows her with slow, measured steps.

                    INT. AIDAN'S PARENTS' HOUSE—KITCHEN
Cool toned colour scheme, everything pristinely clean and well kept, but the room is small. There is a small table with two chairs pushed up against a window. Aidan's mum is at the coffee maker, pouring herself a cup of coffee. Aidan appears at the door.

AIDAN: I'm good, thanks.
Aidan's mum shrugs, and sits on one of the chairs. Aidan stays standing awkwardly near the door. He doesn't take off his coat or scarf, and his mum doesn't invite him to. Silence.

AIDAN(CONT'D): Where's Dad?

MUM: Market.

AIDAN: Oh. But I asked you both to be here.

MUM: You were late, and all the half-decent fruit would be gone if he didn't hurry. Aidan rubs his eyes in frustration.

MUM (CONT'D): So how are you? How is Steph? Are you still in the honeymoon phase of things?

AIDAN:(distracted) Good. Good. He's good. Yes, it's lovely, still lovely...
(smiles, and brings his hand up to look at his brand new wedding ring)
Listen, we...

MUM: (chuckling) Who'd have thought... After all these years... But I am glad, Aidan. I really am. See, it all worked out all right in the end.

AIDAN: (a little startled) It did, didn't it?
They stay silent for a moment, but it's a more companionable silence than the previous one. They are more relaxed.

AIDAN: Mum, we need to talk.
She turns to look at him, smiling. But before Aidan can speak, the doorbell rings.

MUM: Oh, be a love and get it for me, will you? It'll be your sister.

INT. AIDAN'S PARENTS' HOUSE—HALLWAY
Aidan opens the door, annoyed and frustrated. MAGGIE, Aidan's younger sister, walks in.

MAGGIE: Oh, hello.(hugging him) Didn't expect to see you here.

AIDAN: (returning her hug distractedly) Hi there. Yes, well...

Maggie steps around him, and walks briskly into the kitchen, almost like a small whirlwind. Aidan pauses. He can hear Maggie greeting their mum. He shuts the door, and follows her into the kitchen.

INT. AIDAN'S PARENTS' HOUSE—KITCHEN

MAGGIE: (taking off her coat, then serving herself coffee from the coffee maker, and sitting opposite their Mum)
Rafal had a late shift, poor thing, came home after midnight completely knackered. I let him sleep in, and drove Elle to her playdate.
Aidan walks in slowly, and stays near the door, looking awkward and reserved, still in his coat and scarf, a stark contrast to Maggie's ease. He looks like he wants to talk, to stop this conversation.

MUM: Is he going to pick her up at least? You do everything for Elle, and parenting is a job for two, you know. You work too, you need a lie-in as well every once in a while.

MAGGIE: (rolling her eyes) Yes, I know, but he's a doctor, I can't really be a pest when he's worked a twelve hour shift in the middle of the night, can I?

MUM: Just make sure you have time for yourself, is all.

MAGGIE: Yes, yes. I do this yoga class on Sundays, remember? (suddenly turning to Aidan) How's Steph? You should come round to ours for dinner soon. It's been awhile, hasn't it?

Aidan is startled. He seems a little lost. Opens his mouth to reply. Pauses.

AIDAN: I have cancer.

Silence. A clock can be heard ticking in the background. Aidan's mum drops a teaspoon she was holding, and it bangs on the table as she brings her hands over her mouth. Pause.

AIDAN(CONT'D): Thyroid cancer. It usually isn't such a big deal. They can't be sure how far along it has really progressed, but... It looks like there might be a metastasis in the vocal cords.

The two women are stunned. They remain silent. Aidan's mum's eyes are bright with tears. Aidan's talking at his shoes in a monotonous, almost detached voice.

AIDAN(CONT'D): They will have to operate soon. I'm booked in for next week. Complete thyroid removal. Vocal cords removal as well, if the surgeon thinks it's necessary. The biopsy will show how bad it is. Best case scenario, I have to do radiation therapy. Worse case scenario...

His voice breaks, and he bursts into tears. He stands by the door, sobbing and wiping away tears, trying to regain control but he is unable to. He stands there, his entire frame shaking. His mum's hands appear, and slowly they lower Aidan's hands. They take his face, and turn it towards his mum. She is openly crying now, and Aidan sees it, a little startled. He has somewhat calmed down, but tears are still streaming down his cheeks.

MUM: (whispering) My boy...

She takes his face and brings it down to her neck. She hugs him tight, as he starts sobbing again. They remain like this. Aidan's mum strokes his hair soothing him, as Maggie at the table has buried her face in her hands.

MUM(CONT'D):(whispering in a broken voice)
It'll be all right. You have us. We'll be there, every step. It'll be all right. Oh my boy... My darling boy...

                                                    FADE OUT

SHORT CIRCUIT

Kyle Wakefield

The first thing they did after bringing me out of my coma was congratulate me on my forethought. My insurance plan covered everything: stitching the cuts, setting the broken fingers, repairing the crushed trachea, replacing the head with a silicone and carbon fibre prosthetic. I'd even catalogued a cast of my face during setup, so they could rebuild it down to the very last pore. I was beaten up in the street, they said. The police were investigating, but they knew I wouldn't be any help. They couldn't save my brain.

It's strange. Really, the estuaries of crescent-moon scars on my hands and chest are the only proof they've got the right guy. They programmed the new brain with the essentials—Merle James Kilbride, thirteenth of April two thousand and forty, eight King's Street Brighton, Aviva PLC, a spreadsheet's worth of numbers—but the frivolous memories had to be left to my wife. Was happy to hear I had a wife. Happier when she came to visit, all red hair and red nose and frantic questions. Paloma Kilbride. Beautiful, and unearned.

I ask to attend the autopsy. The two detectives, in their navy pea coats, don't take their eyes off me. I stare down at the head laid on the plastic sheeting, the skin as chemically clean as my new silicone. Around one empty eye-socket, a curved scar that matches the ones on my hands. And the cause of death: a round hole in the centre of the forehead. A hole the diameter of a fist.

"What kind of blade was this?" I ask, tracing the scar.

"They're not cuts," the mortician says, parting the rubbery flesh with his thumbs. "They're crush injuries. From the same round… object that killed you."

He turns the head over, showing me two seams. The first cut from ear to ear, the second sawn around the crown.

"Can I see it?" I ask. "The brain?"

Nodding, he disassembles the head and lifts out the grey mass of brain, which quivers in his hands like a frightened pet. Before, that thing, that lump of meat, held Merle Kilbride, not the copper-veined machine that holds him now.

"Can I hold it?"

He slides the brain into my hands. It's so heavy. And wet, like a mollusc.

"And there's no way of getting the memories back from this?"

"Sorry, Mr Kilbride."

"Can't I upgrade the insurance?"

The detectives are still staring at me. Fifteen years ago, I would've been an engineering marvel, yeah, but now, it's just bad manners. Like staring at a bloke with one leg.

"We think the weapon was improvised," one of them says.

"Improvised?" I ask. "What, on the spot?"

"Yes."

"But wouldn't someone who'd set out to attack someone bring a proper weapon?"

He winces.

•

A month later, it happens again. I wake up in hospital plugged into a hundred whinging machines, none of them monitoring heart rate or brain activity or urine output this time. Was the whole body this time, Mr Kilbride, they tell me, but no worries—insurance covered it all. Just be extra careful in the weeks before the renewal comes through, cos two revivals is the max.

This time, when I ask if they can get back my memories, they nod. The green cards they put in these brains can withstand more monstrous batterings than the black boxes on aeroplanes. They slot it in, and Merle crackles back through the nape of my neck: address, date of birth, national insurance number, the aftermath of the first assault, the autopsy, the rehab, the hours of absorbing photographs and stories with Paloma. But nothing of the second assault besides the sound of the impact, like a car being crushed in a junkyard.

It'll do that, they say. One critical strike on your wiring and it all short-circuits to shit. I swear they build them that way on purpose. So you'll have to pay for a new one every time.

I'm glad I asked to attend the autopsy again. Seeing that much butchered flesh and powdered bone'd make any man glad to be synthetic. Crescent moons again, cuffing my neck, up and down my limbs, skull crushed like an egg, dried blood plastering my shirt into my guts. I ask the detective if he still thinks it was an improvised fucking weapon.

"The assailant left hair at the scene," he says instead. "The DNA isn't on record, but it's female."

I nod.

"Something else," he adds, pulling a photograph from his pocket. It shows the pavement, and three fingers of my hand. Written in blood on the grey stone is the beginnings of a word.

MONST

"Monster?" I say, feeling a cold vibration in my chest. "Is…was that me?"

The detective replaces the photograph in his pocket. "We're not sure who wrote it," he says. "Could've been you about her. Or her about you."

"Why would she? Because of my prosthetic?"

He winces.

•

For weeks, I lie awake at night, plugged into my charger, thinking about Merle. Paloma tells me the assaults changed me. I used to like Avenged Sevenfold and now I like the Black-Eyed Peas. I can't stand the taste of beer, or the hordes of friends that accost me in the street. The man in the wedding photos has too many creases in his face and eyes as dead as glass. She tells me I used to yell and throw things and pin her to walls and call her a dirty whore and now I'm sweet again, as sweet as when we met.

Sometimes, when I feel a plastic bone gliding in its joint, or an organ swelling with a temperature change, I remember this isn't how people are meant to feel. We're meant to be made of unpredictable wet stuff, like the brain I held in my hands. We're meant to get sick and better again and feel things that don't make sense. We're not meant to be this... balanced. But perhaps, in my case, taking all that away was for the best.

•

"In the first assault, you attacked first." The detective shows me a crudely labelled diagram of my wounded hands.

"I don't understand. You told me those were self-defence wounds."

"Well. They are. In a sense. Her defending herself, while you held her."

I shake my head. "Are you sure?"

"Don't worry, Mr Kilbride. You're not legally culpable for anything your old brain did."

"What about the second time? Please tell me the second time was different."

"Yes. The second time was all her. And she meant to kill you."

"Why?" I say. "Why keep hurting me if it wasn't her intention all along?"

The detective puts down his papers and looks at me.

"Revenge," he says, the word stirring another cold rumble in my ribcage. "Do you know what being assaulted does to you, Merle? It makes you feel like your body's not yours, like the pieces don't fit, like someone's burrowed into your meaty core and torn you in half. It can change everything about you. All the malice your brain transplant took from you? It's hers now."

I lick my lips, silicone sliding over silicone. "But I'm different now."

"She obviously doesn't care."

•

I don't know why I wanted a walk. When I look at these streetlights, all my wretched brain wants to know is how much red, green and blue goes into their sickly orange, whether the light is more gas or liquid. The fog doesn't taste of anything, not even cold. I'm only a block from home, but that's where I'm least safe. At sunset, I saw a figure by my garden wall, all bushy hair and square-shouldered coat.

Her footsteps come up behind me, heavy and flat, like her shoes are too big. Then, her hands come over my eyes, her flesh as cold as mine.

"Guess who, honey?" Her breath billows over my shoulder. And without any memory at all, I know that's what I said to her. That night. Before I tore her in two.

"I'm sorry—" I cut myself off with a cry as something metal strikes the small of my back and sticks there. "I'm not... the one who hurt you."

She growls. In one move, she wrenches the weapon free and kicks me to the ground, pressing her boot to my throat as I roll over. I don't recognise her, but I know this isn't my first look at her. The first time I've thought she could be prettier. Complexion yellow-white like wax, dark curls neglected frizzy, bitten lips, doe eyes glazed with rage.

"Merle Kilbride?" she says. "Thirty-five, Eight King's Street Brighton, brown hair, blue eyes? Yes, you fucking are."

She drops and starts to hit me. I scream with every blow, but I don't beg. Sternum, throat, elbows, knees—her weapon splinters their beautiful synthesis of mechanical and biological engineering like a sledgehammer on wooden beams. As I gasp for breath, she pulls my mouth open with one finger and pushes the weapon inside. Heavy. Dented metal, black and green. It's a drinks can. I know the brand. Monster.

"One o'these was all I had," she says, "night you attacked me. Was enough, they said. Enough to save my skin. Nothing else." She laughs. "I don't care if you've got a new brain, new heart, new grabbin' hands, new cock, no matter what the law says, understand? You know what keeps me up at night? The fact you're not just walking round, but walking round without so much as the memories to nag at you. All I can do's keep wrecking you till those wretches stop giving you second chances."

And she takes the can from my mouth and starts driving it into my face. Her fist breaks through rubber and metal and wiring and empty space and hits the stone on the other side.

the city

Oliver Hancock

I don't often walk this way to work since it's longer
(and it's strange to be alone)
But when I do I see things I've missed before, glowing things
    Like the florist filling tin buckets with water from the alley
    And the bakery throwing out yesterday's goods for today's sweets
    And the homeless woman a road over moving to new pastures.
Sometimes (if I'm early enough) I catch the life dimming from streetlights
And I try not to think of when we were out so late that the dusk/dawn
Mingled in a lilac haze and the moon/sun/stars whirled in our heads.

Today I'm late for work because this way is longer
(and I was caught in a memory net)
But here I am climbing above the city in a glass box, things shrinking
    Like the green by your house covered with ants and beetles
    Or the hill where a castle once stood and you can see for miles
    And from there the city looks so huge it would never stop.
I sit at my desk and unpack my things and put a salad in the fridge.

The Great Mew Stone

Flo Pearce-Higginson

Fiona and Fred throw stones at the sea.

Fred wants to make the biggest splash, and so does Fiona.

Seagulls screech above them, and waves gently splash against the drab sand, towed out again and again by the gentle tide. In the rockpools, crabs charge to and fro, anemones squelch, and limpets cling on to their rocks. Nothing will move them.

In the middle of the leaden sea in front of them, encompassed by blue sky and beautiful white clouds, sits the Great Mew Stone. Adorned with patches of brown and green, sharp rocks dotting the far-left edge of the island, the Stone slants down on one side, like a cake that has sunken halfway through baking.

Fiona and Fred don't think much of the Stone. They're more interested in the fact that Fred has just spotted a jellyfish which has washed up on the shoreline. Off they race, shrieking with glee, seeking a suitable piece of driftwood to poke the jellyfish with. It's almost as if they don't know what today means.

Their dad, Martin, sits on a rock further up the beach. He gazes at his two young children, just past their seventh birthday, as they zip along the wet sand, their footsteps trailing behind them. It is a beautiful day, with the sun beaming down over everyone, and only a little wind to rustle the trees. But inside, Martin feels empty. Or at least, he is trying to feel empty. Today is thirty years. Thirty years since Dad passed. He should feel…sad? Angry? Lonely? He isn't really sure. He should certainly be feeling something.

Martin feels he should try to talk to Fiona and Fred about Dad. Just so that they know who he was, and that he was a kind, gentle man. Sighing, he raises himself off the rock. Fiona and Fred appear to be poking a jellyfish, and Martin really doesn't fancy a hospital trip due to a nasty sting.

***

'Daddy?'

'Yes, Fred?'

'Who lives there?'

'Where?'

'On the big rock.'

Fiona glances up, temporarily distracted from the jellyfish, to gaze out at the Great Mew Stone. She can't see a house on it, only birds and grass. Maybe there is one on the other side, Fiona ponders.

'No one lives there, darling. There was a man living there once, all alone. But he's gone now,' Martin utters.

Fred stares down at his wellington boots, twisting a bit of seaweed around his fingers in the simultaneously absent minded and deeply focused way children often do when fidgeting.

'Does anyone ever go there? In a boat?' asks Fred.

'No. Sometimes people sail around it, but you can't land there. Only the birds live there.'

'Ok, Daddy.'

Martin chews the inside of his lip, wondering what to say about Dad. The children start racing off down the beach, and Martin quickly gives chase, his mind still buzzing.

***

As the day carries on, the sun falls lower and lower until the Stone is illuminated, pitch black, against the sea stained beautifully orange by the sunset. Fred and Fiona have wanted to go home for hours, but Martin doesn't want to leave just yet.

'What's the matter, Daddy? I'm cold!' demands Fiona.

'Me too! I want to go home!' Fred yells, and they begin a chorus, shrieking 'We want to go home!' in unison. Martin remains silent, staring out at the Stone.

A single tear courses its way down his face, catching in his beard. Fiona stops shouting at the sight of it and places her hand on her twin's arm to silence him.

'Daddy? Are you crying? Why?'

Martin sniffs, hastily brushing the tear away. 'Come here, sit with Daddy. And I'll tell you.'

They scuttle to his side, Fred settling himself on his father's lap, with Fiona snuggled under his arm.

'Do you remember this morning, when I told you that today was a special day? Well, today is thirty years since your grandpa died. My daddy.'

'Thirty years, Daddy? That's so long! That's older than you!' Fred smirks. Martin chuckles, rubbing his son's golden hair.

'Not quite. Daddy is a bit older than that. Anyway, we came here today because this beach was very special to your grandpa. When he was still alive, he used to come here with Granny and collect samples of sea creatures for his lab. And then, when he died, they built a Marine Centre in his memory, and put his name over the door.'

'So he will always be here?' asks Fred.

'So he will always be here.'

Fred gazes absently at his Daddy, enjoying the story but not really sure what to say. Fiona reaches up and touches her father's face, his beard rough under her fingers.

'That's good, Daddy. I want to see Grandpa. He sounds nice.'

'He was. But you can't see him. I really wish we could. Even just for a minute.' Martin feels the pain rising in his throat, and his eyes begin to burn. Hot, steaming tears rush down his face again, and his chest tightens.

Peering across the water at the Stone, Martin is struck by an idea. Glimpsing down at his children's beautiful faces, flooded with the evening light, he quickly brushes his tears away, takes a deep breath, and tries to explain.

'Grandpa is like the Great Mew Stone. The big rock in the sea. We can see him, and we can always come and visit him, and he will still be there. But we cannot go to him. It's…not our place. Not yet. You won't go there for years and years, and neither will I.' Fiona nods her head, even though she doesn't really understand. How can Grandpa be the same as a rock? And when will she and Fred go? What is there?

Fred already feels he understands a bit better. Grandpa had been here, and now he wasn't. And that makes Daddy very sad. Maybe one day, Fred thought, he will be sad like Daddy. He hopes not.

'Come on, Daddy. Let's go home.' Fiona leaps down from the rock, beckoning Fred to follow her so that they can race up the beach to the car. Off they dash, leaving their father alone.

Martin takes in the fantastic sight of the sun setting over the Great Mew Stone once more, and turns to follow his children. As much as he wishes he could stay there forever to think of who was gone, new life and new noise are with him now.

The Hotel of Exchanges
Aisla McKenzie

If you find yourself alone at a bus stop, far from the crowds and the prying eyes, you should try waiting for a while. There is a good chance that a certain coach will pull up.

You will not remember what colour it is, nor will you remember if you saw a driver, but you will remember that a kindly old man showed you to your seat.

There will be someone sat next to you who will ask you what you have to offer. Do not be alarmed, no one there will rob you. You may show them what you have if you wish.

You will then arrive at a hotel, standing alone in one of its corridors. This is the Hotel of Exchanges. You will not remember what the hotel looked like from the outside, nor will you remember how you got to where you are.

A well-dressed attendant will walk past you. You must follow them; they will show you to your room. You will not remember their face.

Inside will be a king size bed, a round table with two chairs, and a bathroom. You may stay in this room for as long as you like, however, you will not be able to leave until you present something with which to exchange. You may exchange anything you wish, there is but one rule; whatever you exchange must be of value to you.

If you should choose to exchange an object, you must place it on the table and sit in the chair facing away from the door. If you wish to exchange a piece of yourself, you will find the necessary tools to do so in the bathroom cabinet. If what you offer is not something physical, you may write it down using the notepad and pen that will be available on the table. If you should choose to offer the use of your body, you are to present yourself naked on the bed. Though be warned, if the rule is not followed, no one will enter your room in order to make the exchange.

The nature of the client who will enter will vary depending on the nature of what you are offering. Some clients will appear to be as normal and civilized as you and I, while others will be beyond your comprehension. Regardless, this is a place of respect, and you will do well to remember this.

The value of what you offer will determine the value of what you receive. You do not make requests here; they will know better than you what you are looking for. If you are disappointed in what you have received, then you have overestimated the value of what you have offered.

Once the client has left you may clean yourself up in the bathroom should you need to, but you should leave as soon as possible. If you hear a knock at the door, your time is running out. If you hear a knock for the third time, you have over-stayed your welcome and will not be allowed back.

Once you have stepped through the door, you will be returned to your life. You will not remember how you were returned, and you will not recall the time when you were at the hotel. However, you will know that you were there and you will remember how to return.

THE POET

Kyle Wakefield

He was a poet just because he made his journals rhyme,
But when it came to baring soul, he never found the time.
He woke; he dressed; he never aged; his hair was dark and wild;
The drum of heart inside his skull was what he most reviled.

By day he lay, blankets in mouth to stifle dark its glow.
By night it shone through eye and flesh and undulated slow.
The red of it like sunlit ears, the throng of veins a web,
The heat of life trapped in his skin to shudder him to death.

He was a monster, that he knew, with mandibles pressed deep,
Fangs squirrelled in the hinge of jaw to torture him in sleep.
He breathed the night like water when the pressure made him creep,
And wanted old physicians to bleed him with a leech.

He reached his tongue back, daggered, to rend open his throat,
Release the bubbles in his voice and make his feelings float.
He ate and drank to pass the time, endured the guilt and bloat,
And on the hungry, thirsty days, he sat at desk and wrote.

His butchery spoilt paper reams whene'er he coughed and bled, for
The spots of blood would wink at him and then, like smiles, spread.
War-cries were made, stained sheets snatched up, but all the pad was clotted;
His desk was dark, the floor, the pipes; below him, fresh food rotted,

And when night fell, the new red stains glowed heav'nly and carotid.

He tended to the tavern guests see'ng visions in his murk,
He bought fresh food, bound tight his cuts and sang to keep from work,
For butchery was not his fear, nor debt or hate or nurses,
But gath'ring pages stained with blood and reading out the verses.

The glow filled him like mania; it fired his eyes and hands;
It lit the hearths in all his homes and answered his demands;
The glow wrought tomes in nonsense runes that no-one else could read,
But, reading with infernal eyes, he felt genius indeed.

He stored the poems beneath his bed till volume turned to blight;
His room stuffed up with papers, like a body stuffed with light.
A molten fever, iron flesh, his bowels and stomach slurry;
His lips burned brands on lovers' throats when he was in a hurry.

Now, when he wrote, he wrote on ash; he melted holes through pens,
Through metal tube and cartridge-case, made black ink bulge from veins.
His hundredth birthday came and went, his beauty mummified;
He lit up everything he touched, breathed fire when he cried.

Blue flames cavorted on his tongue and arteries were fuses.
He unzipped seams across his chest and peeled off sheets of bruises.
These skin-sheets were immune to fire and loved the taste of words,
And didn't laugh like paper at the nonsense that they heard.

One layer of armour peeled off, his heart became afraid,
And dug itself down deeper still, sequest'ring light in shade.
The poet needed light to write, so he took off his flesh—
Unwound the muscles one by one and laid them on the desk.
(In his bedroom, after all, why should a man be dressed?)

With skin for paper, flesh for cloth and blood clots in his quill,
He wrote and wrote, but heart and light dug deeper, deeper still.
He blamed the quill, so took his knife, turned fingernails to nibs,
Peeled fingers open, wrote with those; his heart kicked at his ribs;

He clawed for it, with talon-fingers, roaring in his rage,
Desp'rate to seize that divine glow and crush it to his page,
To write his lines in righteous fire—but then gave up his fight.
His hands could seize, could grab, no more. All they could do was write.

He kept few friends, but hoarded love, and gossip, and acclaim;
The least a fleshless man deserves is parties in his name.
When asked the secret of his craft, he tried to show his nails,
And gesture to his bleach-white bones, his arms full of entrails;
When no-one saw, he sighed and said, "My secrets aren't for sale."

the ugliest parts

Lucy McEleney

PART 1

I will love the ugliest parts of you
as though they were my food—
live off goodness and beauty,
and the rest of it too.

I find worship in scars, stretch-marks and bruises,
taking each and every one to be my muses;
the oil of your skin and the grease in your hair
as if no other dirt in the world could compare.

The smell of your sweat and the sleep in your eyes
guide me through city soot and office morning sighs.
I could live in the gaps of cracked knuckle and rough skin,
build a home from aching bones where we can both begin.

I'll love the grime in your fingernails
and the mud on your shoe,
I will love the way old couples do,
not because we're stuck, but because we know each other.
Then I'll love the brown spots decorating your hands,
love you until neither of us can stand.

To love the ugliest parts of you would be my delight.
They say we're not pretty, but I know we're alright.

PART 2

Give me tears, snot,
and truly rotten feelings.
Picked apart to the bone by every error,
show me why we shouldn't be together,
and I swear to you I'll stay.

I'll love the ugliest parts of you
until I have nothing else left.
Leave me broken, blazing, out of breath.
Leave me ruptured, leave me bereft,
balanced on the verge of death.

The Vigilante

Billy White

My name is Damon Hollis and I am lying on a basement floor with two 9 mm bullets in my right shoulder and another in my heart.

I am experiencing something akin to a life review. You know what I mean. Supposedly, a person's life story 'flashes before their eyes' in the moments before their death, as the brain frantically searches for a way of averting it. That isn't quite what's happening to me. I am viewing only a fraction of my depressingly short life, mainly the events of the past two days. And instead of feeling any sense of serenity and fulfilment, I'm thinking, 'God almighty, I've really fucked this up.'

Without wanting to sound too sorry for myself, my life has been an almost unmitigated fuck-up. Lying on a basement floor with a bullet in your heart is about as fucked as you can get. And I am in this sorry situation because I became a vigilante.

I am certain that almost every teenage boy in the Western world, including my younger self, is under the impression that being a vigilante is, well, 'cool'. I mean, look at popular culture. Whether it's Robin Hood, Batman, or, for the more murderously inclined, the Punisher, the vigilante has always captured people's imaginations. Note the word 'imagination'. It is only because of imagination that anyone believes vigilantism is 'cool'. I have just found out in the hardest way possible that, assuming you value your life, vigilantism is the very antithesis of 'cool'. In fact, I realise now, the only way one becomes a vigilante is by being a downright loser.

Now for the backstory. I was born in the good old US of A, which my father always said was the greatest country in the world. He may well have been right, but we weren't exactly living in Beverly Hills. For generations, my family have been residents of Hammond, Louisiana, a state which bears the dubious honour of having the highest homicide rate in the entire country. And yes, the numbers of overdoses and Young Earth creationists don't bear thinking about, but for me, things weren't too bad. I got by, I surviving on a diet of hot dogs and comic books.

Things went south, when I was twelve. My parents were good people, but both drank more than is advisable and, driving home from a bar one night, my father wrapped the car around a lamppost, killing himself and my mother almost instantly.

The next few years were the worst of my life. I didn't have any relatives able or willing to take me in, so I ended up in Hammond's foster care system, which provides the kind of upbringing no child deserves. There were fistfights and dead school friends and stuff I don't want to talk about. My only relief during those terrible years was reading the aforementioned comic books. Those things were my goddamn lifeblood. I was in dire need of escapism, and the comics spoke to me. It wasn't just that the colourful pictures and cheesy dialogue brought light into my otherwise bleak world. Nor was it that I identified with the heroes cause most of them had dead parents. I loved the stories because in them, justice always prevailed. The good guys won and nobody died unless they deserved to. It's cornier than the comics themselves, but when I was reading, I wasn't Damon Hollis, the skinny teenager who'd be lucky to get a job at Walmart. I was a superhero.

I wasn't a superhero in real life, though, however much I wanted to be one. No radioactive spider or cosmic power ring came my way. I had to grow up a bit.

That brings me to the present day. I'm twenty-eight now, and I've lived my whole life in Hammond, working a series of dead-end fast food jobs. I'd still be doing that were it not for the events of the past two days.

I'm sorry to keep jumping around, but the tragic case of Zoe Turner is a crucial part of my ill-fated journey. It happened a few weeks ago. Zoe was seven years old when she vanished while playing in her front garden. It happened only a few blocks from my own house, so naturally I followed the story. It wasn't pleasant. She was black, which may explain why the police did nothing, and after a week she was found dead a few blocks away. The post-mortem revealed she'd been sexually assaulted.

According to local gossip, the prime suspect was Zoe's neighbour, Isaiah Douglas. People said he'd been overly friendly towards the girl several times, and the police's search of his computer revealed some images of children which were certainly illegal. To me, at least, it was obvious Douglas was guilty. But no forensic evidence could be found, and he was released. The son of a bitch even had the nerve to claim a friend had downloaded the pictures while borrowing the computer. Then everyone more or less forgot about the whole thing. Everyone, that is, except me.

When Isaiah Douglas walked free, something inside me just snapped. What kind of monster could commit a crime like that, and how could the cops do nothing? It was all I thought about for weeks, until, two days ago, I made my decision. I'd do what the justice system wouldn't, and put Isaiah Douglas down like the animal he was. I couldn't be a superhero, but I could be the next best thing.

I made my preparations. I already had a gun, a Glock 19. It was a common model, but it would do the job. The only other thing I needed was to protect my identity, so I went to a dollar store and bought a ski mask. I did think about painting a skull or something on my chest, but then I thought better of it. All I needed to do was get in, kill Douglas, and get away.

So yesterday I went for a walk around Douglas's neighbourhood. I asked someone where he lived, disguising my interest as idle chit-chat. His house was little more than a shack, and the front door looked so old I was certain I could break it down. I might have gone in straight away, but I'd forgotten the mask, so I decided to come back the following evening when I'd have less chance of being identified. That would be the night I avenged Zoe Turner, I thought. It's almost funny now, how wrong I was.

All of that brings us to today. At 9 PM, I decided it was time. A feeling of Zen-like calm had come over me. None of the flaws in my plan even crossed my mind. Douglas might not have been home. There might have been someone else in the house. I might even have misremembered the address. I got lucky on all three of those counts, but it didn't end up doing me much good.

I put on the mask and went to the house. There were noises coming from inside that must have been the TV. I took a deep breath, walked up to the door and rammed my shoulder into it. It hurt more than I expected, but I persisted, slamming myself into the wood again and again until it splintered. I stepped through and found myself in a dim hallway, keenly aware of how much noise I had made. Isaiah Douglas stood in front of me. He was a small African American man, a few years older than me, and it delighted me to see the panic in his face. I stared him down for a second, and he said, 'Shit. You want money?'

'I'm here because of Zoe Turner,' I replied, and reached for the gun.

His eyes widened and he turned and ran, sprinting along the hallway and down a flight of stairs. I pulled out the Glock and followed him. The stairs led to a basement, perhaps the place where Douglas had done those terrible things to Zoe. He was in a corner, desperately trying to yank open a drawer. I took aim and pulled the trigger.

I heard once that the loudest sounds are a bang when you're expecting a click, and a click when you're expecting a bang. The latter was true for me. I stood there for what felt like an eternity, realising I hadn't shot Douglas and never would, because I had left the safety on.

Douglas found what he was looking for, a gun which I briefly recognised as a Glock like my own. He brought it round and fired twice, and twice I felt a pain in my shoulder like I'd been hit with a sledgehammer. I twisted and fell backwards, and as I did so Douglas shot me in the heart. I hit the floor. Then my life review began.

I saw with total clarity what a fool I'd been. Not in leaving the safety on, not even in my decision to become a vigilante, but my whole life. All my dreams of being a hero had been delusions. There was nothing cool about taking the law into your own hands, and the only reason I'd thought otherwise was because I was a sad, lonely no-hoper who'd read too many fucking comic books. And that's the end of my story. I guess the moral is, don't be like me. I wish I could say I see my parents' faces in front of me, but I don't. I don't see anything.

*

Isaiah Douglas could not take his eyes off the body that lay on the floor of his basement. For a few seconds the dying man had spluttered uselessly at the air, as if he was trying to articulate some last words to an unseen audience. But he would never speak again. Douglas dropped his gun with a clatter, drew a shuddering breath, and said, 'Jesus.' Then he went upstairs and called the police.

THE SIREN SONG

Beth Lane

Her mellow lullaby rolls over sea ripples,
Acoustic caramel,
You gasp as snowy doves triple,
Near moth-eaten sails.
Hazy thoughts of her scarlet lips,
You drool from the mouth,
Through the night her melody rips,
Her promises heading south.
O' how you gush and plea!
Her songs make rotten crops bloom,
You cannot help but thirst for she
And claim her voice calms typhoons.
You foolish, lustful boy,
Trailing after her sorrowful tune,
Eyes wide with greed, ever so coy
Did you think you would be immune?
Pale lips are scarlet from tearing throats,
Teeth inches into plump flesh,
Cloudy slits of eyes gloat,
She swallows blood that is so sweet, so fresh.
She would peel your skin like a tangerine,
Make instruments with your frail bones.
I ask you; will that make you preen?
At least your body is now in her home.
Or will you see with your wisdom,
She yearns to pry apart your ribs,
Insane with delusion,
In your slimy heart she digs.
Yes, she may lick its begging pulse;
May slobber over its edges,
Now you realise it was false—
Your bloody doom is all she pledges.
But I know daft beings like you,
Even as she gnaws at your leg, neck, wrist,
You would still let her boil you into stew,
While fantasising about her dreamy kiss.

Thisday
Kathy Floyd

She's not got long to go now, they said. Victoria phoned yesterday when I was cutting up Death of the Author. She's mother's favourite, is big Vic. The one who always kissed her goodnight, said sod it to the rules. The plump one, you know the sort, type two diabetes from Mulbarton, lesbian married daughter in Eastbourne, heart in that good place. Mother prefers real life stories to TV rubbish. I think when they know they're a Do Not Resuscitate resident, they linger longer, reveal more, forget themselves.

I was in bed drinking, making her roll-ups out of habit, half listening to that Jenny Harries who's always on the telly now at 6pm with Whitty and Valance and Hancock and Boris, half waiting for the Home to phone again. What an emotionally devoid human specimen Harries is, and now she's hammering home Test Test Test, and the other week she was saying we didn't need to Test Test Test because we were a first world country, and Cheltenham was no strong danger.

Right.

They won't let mother smoke straights anymore. Not since she nodded off with the thing between her yellowed fingers and set fire to her blanket. I had to buy her a welder's apron off Amazon after that. Dead animal skin thing mustard suede. Her fingers blend into it till you don't know they're there. Only ever takes it off for bed at seven, after potions and lotions are dispensed and absorbed.

Doctor Rasmina confirmed it. Yes, she'll probably be gone by tomorrow, she said. No, a hospital admission isn't an option. Your mother's ninety-six the twentysomething GP said. She's had a good life, it's a wonderful age. What would she know? Have you read Death of the Mother, I asked her. She apologised for having to 'bring the call to an end'.

Mother's certificate for Full Mental Capacity got shredded five years ago around the time Trump announced his intention to stand for president. She's had COPD half her life and smoked forever. Now they're saying nicotine is a good thing on the news, roll up, roll up.

People try and pull you up. You don't really spill, but you find yourself bent over the screen searching for a virtual handhold. The Brancott Estate on offer at Tesco slides down a treat again and you're connecting, linking something immediately meaningful that comes into your head, just like that, Tommy Cooper style. Glug glug. You offer your friends Eric Carmen, All by Myself. Let Eric sing what you can't say. Sometimes people can't be bothered to navigate to the red heart with their overworked fingers, so they just click on the thumbs up cos they feel obliged to respond. 'Hey, I get that' they say, job done, moving on, not looking back. Sometimes they might. Who knows? You forage for what you had, what and who you were, how it was, why it went the way it did. Something escaped and we all got trapped. Life, suddenly so precious, or is it?

Depends on the quality I guess.

Sometimes you really fucking laugh OUT LOUD. HA HA HA, HA HA HA

HA in your head and in the hollow tap tap of the haha language you use to half-heartedly connect communicate or disconnect. Stuff comes out of the blue, into your blue, morphing into your own shit, muddying it. You turn to see your face in the dusty mirror of isolation. Former friend, perpetual reflector and af-firmer of a life going somewhere, not just anywhere, nowhere.

Clichés rule the right side of your brain where art stuff should happen and the logical left left you ages ago. Bereft. You follow the rules though. You practice deeper reverence: the returning blossom, birdsong, cleaner air, functioning lungs, toilet rolls. You linger on your own front path like it's the walkway to Blickling Hall and dance around an imaginary Chelsea Girl clutch bag in your kitchen to 'I Will Survive'. It got you through when you were dumped at seventeen. Will it now? You fancy yourself as Agnetha from ABBA. Lay All Your Love On Me blasts out. Glug. You have her blue eyes. You get carried away with the volume and your mother comes back to haunt you. Maybe she will. She's opened the bedroom door. Caught you trying out life at thirteen, when you were confused and pissed, like you are now:

Stands in the doorway, arms folded, apron stained from yesterday's gravy. Yesterday's news. Your father's not coming back. Slam. You can hear her back-downstairs, stuff smashing, cupboards emptying, doors banging. Slam smash bang. Swig. She can't hear your laboured breathing through the din she makes, see your fingers jamming your ears shut, see the rainbows on your wallpaper blur and fade.

Forty years on and here's the dog's standing in the doorway, ears erect, dinner face on: Good job you've got me, she says. Who else can love you like this? Who else to steal heat from on frosty April mornings when nightmares banish sleep and sheep bleat, bugger off, we don't want to be counted? She lays all her love on me as I open and bin the tin without remembering how the food reached the plate of the placater.

I tried this experiment yesterday. It's all to do with experimental writing, what-ever that is. What you've got to do is get a load of stuff together, newspapers, old love letters, your mother's will, deeds to your house, study books, blah blah. You just have to cut up the sentences, mix them about on the floor and then rearrange them to remake meaning. I shredded Barthes and a Chat mag. Here's the start of mine. Da Dah!

The text is a tissue of quotations and instructions for making your own mask drawn from Aunty Nelly's Problem Page. Unsure of my vagina diagnosis, each of us has his own rhythm of suffering and language is never innocent. Man does not exist prior to language, subscribe to Chat from just £10.99* refer to the small print. The author enters into his own death, from Jumbo Jess to Pretty Princess, writing begins and dad's trousers save the wedding. The new is not a fashion, it is a value, and only 9% of Britons want to return to normal after lockdown is over to get £50 of FREE BINGO or 30 Free Spins.

I should be doing the essay, changing my sheets, feeding myself, bagging up the dog shit, cleaning the mirror, moving on. Glug glug.

They say an active brain keeps dementia away. 2000 words please on how your chosen text develops a variety of Realism. Use a prompt to get you into the spirit of the thing guys: Choose from: Stay at Home, Save Lives, Protect the NHS, Ramping Up, These Unprecedented Times, or Test, Track and Trace. Not really. Perspective, The Everyday and Social Totality are the boys to look out for in this essay. All part of the same fruit cake right now.

My mother never removed her wedding ring after the divorce. Lord, no, what would people think for goodness sake, that was the 70s. Poor Miss Brill never even got the opportunity to don the gold band. Some numb head from the uni unthinkingly married off Mansfield's brilliant creation and renamed her Mrs Brill in the study guide.

I mean.

It's enough to make you want to give up. And what the hell does the Everyday mean anymore? It's either Thisday Thatday Someday or Oneday and remote learning makes me feel   remote.

Head hurts.

Swig. Maybe I should go over, high thread count tea-towel tied round my face, smash my way in, smother my mother in a final spray of goodbye kisses? Lay the rest of my love on her. God knows, there's plenty left for the taking.

I'm going a bit askew alone here with the dog and all the cut-up pieces of paper and mixed messages all over the floor, the tele, the radio, the internet. The stats of the dead and dying, obligatory chats, same old, murky new.

Unscrew another cap.

I haven't seen her for a month now. Last time was no different to usual. A continued rampage of rage under the guise of her progressive neurological disorder. I never asked her about dad, why he left—whether it was my fault, what with me being his 'nightmare of a teenager', but I probably was the reason. I would have liked to tell her about the dried gravy on her pinny, about what the memory of it means to me now I'm as old as she was when life took a turn for the worst, and she was abandoned. I'd like to tell her about how that apron kept me going, unconsciously, knowing other tea-times would come. Tell her I know she did her best, even on the blackest of days. Like when she didn't leave her bed till I came home from school, when the weight of the apron was too much, and we sat in silence, distanced on the sagging settee, dining on sugar sandwiches and tinned peaches. But they won't let me in to love her and she can't understand why, and I've had to stop phoning because all she says, shouts, is, 'Why don't you come anymore'.

There goes the phone. I'm not ready for this. Dizzy head again. Seventh ring and the answer machine kicks in. I push my palms hard to my ears, sing LA LA LA LA LA LA LA over and over. *GO AWAY.*

Hi Bethany, tha's Vic at The Laurels here, was really hopin to catch ya, ring me back soon as you can, will ya? We had to call in Doctor Rasmina cos your mother's taken a turn again. She's actually, like, you won't believe it, sat up in bed right now, askin for ice-cream and wantin to know when you'll be droppin off her rollies, habloodyha. No rush on that front. We're like, gobsmacked here. Speak soon Byeee.

Thuy
Megan Dennison

On the outskirts of Ho Chi Minh City, Vietnam. 1986.

Thuy navigated her way down the rocky path. The one that ran parallel with the water. She made a conscious effort to avoid the muddy patches and dodged the bigger stones that could have sent her tumbling straight down the hill. She wasn't in a rush for anyone. She wanted to be completely sure of what she was about to do and who she was about to meet.

As she walked, Thuy untangled her hair. She remembered her mother scraping it back into a tight bun at the base of her head as a little girl. The long, harsh strokes she would take, not leaving a single strand out of place. You must take care of it, she'd say. It is the most beautiful thing you have. Thuy grew up admiring her mother's hair. The wooden wide-toothed comb she would brush it with, the small vial of oil she would massage into her roots each night before bed, and the way it fell to the small of her back in one sweeping motion. It was a ritual. And watching it every day always brought the same thought. Just how much she would love to take a sharp pair of scissors to it.

Thuy was almost halfway to the meeting point when she realised she'd have to show her parents what she had done. She could already see the frown of her father's eyebrows and feel the sting on her left cheek. But part of her couldn't wait to prove that she could undo everything they wanted. And by the time she had made it to the end of the path, she was decided.

She would watch her hair fall to the ground.

On the other side of the market, where the path opened up, a small man stood impatiently beside his silver motorbike, his helmet on, as though he was prepared to leave at any moment. Thuy refused to walk any faster to catch up with him. She wanted to savour these last moments with her hair and remind herself of its worth, so she wouldn't let it go for any less than it deserved. But before she was within five metres of the man, he had already seen her.

"Thuy?" he said, her unsettled expression giving her away. Thuy stepped closer, noticing the man's small, pointed chin and high cheekbones. He pulled a hand away from the motorbike and reached out for hers in greeting.

A woman's name fell from her mouth. "Bian," she said. A woman of secrets.

Thuy blushed at her mistake, feeling immediately at ease in another woman's presence and reached out to shake her hand in return. Bian leaned forward, pulling half of Thuy's hair in front of her right shoulder and letting it glide through her palms.

"Virgin hair. Good," she said, half smiling. Bian's accent was not purely Vietnamese, distracting Thuy for a moment. American, she thought. That's it.

"Will it be worth more, then?" Thuy broke her silence, forgetting when she last heard her own voice out loud.

"You would be best off if we take twenty inches. Hai mưở'i inch. Yes?"

"Twenty?" Thuy questioned herself in whisper, remembering what her mother had told her, that each half inch marked a month's growth. Three years, she worked out, which didn't add up. Thuy nodded at Bian, more concerned that her hair hadn't kept up with her mother's. "How much will you give me for it?" she probed.

"You'd be lucky to get more than ten dollars from buyers out there," Bian answered, shuffling around in her leather jacket to find the white paper envelope stashed away there, "but I can do a little over a hundred."

Thuy kept her eyes fixated on Bian's hands, which expertly counted each note in the stack, not remembering ever having held that much money of her own. "How little over?" Thuy asked, stalling a bit.

Bian paused to look up at Thuy, as if offended by the question, but soon returned to her counting. "Six," she confirmed, "one hundred and six. Một trăm lẻ sáu."

A few silent moments passed between the pair before they headed down a concrete alley behind the sheltered stalls lined up in the market. They hunted for a patch of quiet, Bian wheeling her bike slowly by her side, Thuy trying not to walk ahead.

"Here," Bian finally stopped and signalled to a small, paved staircase ahead of them. Thuy admired her decisiveness. Bian seemed like a woman of free will and she wondered what that must be like. They walked some more until they reached the steps, which led to a locked door and were overgrown with weeds. There was something beautiful about the way its green veins pulled apart the grout and crumbled away the stone, Thuy thought. Nature taking over.

Thuy carefully took a seat on a lower step as Bian kicked the stand down on her bike, leaning it towards the brick wall beside them. She took off her helmet, revealing her short, blunt cut. Just looking at it, Thuy could feel the weight of her own hair on her shoulders. She ran her fingers through the knots for the last time, each tug pulling at her scalp. From the back of the bike, Bian pulled out a folded black pouch, opening it up on the tallest step to reveal her tools: a silver pair of scissors, a plastic orange comb, some small zip ties in a sandwich bag, a small pocket mirror, and five hair clips. Bian examined its contents, checking she hadn't forgotten anything. Not that she ever did.

"Okay," Bian muttered, "let's start."

* * *

Hair holds trauma in its roots. Each inch marks another month in hurtful hands. And the fallen strands are stolen words. Stories. A woman silenced by her husband. A daughter hit by her father for challenging authority. Femininity. Beauty. Submission.

Bian lifts her scissors from the step and they fall perfectly onto finger and thumb. With the same hand she holds her comb, brushing the length of Thuy's hair. She does this thoroughly, taking her time. As the thick, black river flows between her hands, so does the woman's story it belongs to. The musky air of the suburbs surrounding Ho Chi Minh City, Vietnam. The constant dryness it brings with it. The warm, meaty scent of bò kho cooking on the stove. The unspoken tension between her mother and father, brewing, as they eat. The endless wait until he finishes his meal, always having seconds. The deep booming voice that fills their home as she tries to sleep. The one of anger and threat. Both women lying awake in fear of night. Or day. Or both.

Bian feels these moments all at once, as though she has lived them herself. The familiarity of sitting on the shelf of your own life, scared your middle pages will be torn out for telling the wrong truths. She can't help but consider whether she is being robbed of her own story each time she leaves with the hair of another woman. But she is willing to lose part of herself in their freedom. She is one and all of them at once.

***

Few words were exchanged in the hour that followed, and Bian let Thuy find comfort in the silence. She knew there was safety in gentle hands. By the time the last section was cut, Bian could sense Thuy's face turn from hesitation to liberation. She watched her twisting the ends, which were now sitting just above her shoulders, almost as though she wanted to protect them. Their fresh beginnings.

"They feel healthier. Stronger," Thuy said, nodding and laughing nervously. She watched as Bian collected all the cuttings, each section neatly secured with a zip tie, placing them inside the sandwich bag.

Bian was certain Thuy was so distracted that she would forget to ask for the money, but soon recognised that her reluctance to leave was due to the realisation that her hair was gone for good. Or, that she was confiding in a person and being understood.

"Here," Bian said, reaching back into her pocket to retrieve the envelope and passing it over.

"Cảm o'n bạn," Thuy responded, accepting the money as her end of the deal, seeming unsure whether 'thank you' were the right words.

"What will you use it for. The money? It's a lot to spend in a place this small." Bian felt attached to Thuy's response and the pause unsettled her.

"A plane ticket," Thuy said, at last. "To Europe."

"What is there for you in Europe? A man?" Bian asked with the tone only a mother knew how to use.

"No. No man."

The two women exchanged their goodbyes, knowing they would never see each other again, having no reason to. The last of the day's sunlight was fading away, and as quickly as she had come into Bian's life, Thuy was gone from it.

Bian rode back until she reached the front gate of the apartment complex she was staying in. She locked up her bike and took the death-defying lift to the seventh floor. She fumbled around for her keys and unlocked the door, closing the blinds on the day and turning on dimmed lamps. Before she forgot, she made her way into the spare room, which was filled with mannequin heads and wigs. To the right, there sat a tall set of office drawers, labelled alphabetically. She pulled at the one labelled

'S-Z', the metal clanging against itself as she did. Running her fingertips along the plastic separators, she searched for the right spot. "Suong, Tam, Than ha, Tien—'' she whispered the names in concentration, pulling back the one before to place a new label, "Thuy".

* * *

Berlin, Germany. 2016.

Thuy liked the kindness strangers offered her here, expecting nothing in return. She liked the supermarkets that blew cool air at her on the way in and consulting her own list on the way round. The artwork on the sides of buildings, appearing overnight, like magic. The short walk to the park from her apartment she took each Sunday, breathing in Spring and letting it bloom. The money in her account. The portion she had sent home—một trăm lẻ sáu—every month, without fail, until her mother died. Always without a note.

The joy of small freedoms.

And as she sat there on the green, her bright coat caught the sun. Intricate embroidery travelled around her arms until it met at the back, spiralling down into the shape of a tree trunk; old and beautiful, like her. Strands of short black hair fell into her face, but you could just about glimpse her dark brown eyes which looked about her with intention. She sat peacefully, on her knees, protected by a golden maple. The light flickered through its leaves, dancing between the sequins on her clothes, warming and sustaining her in that moment. She felt as though she belonged to that very spot, rooted, with the calmness of the branches, their shadows tracking time as they swayed gently in the breeze.

Of all the people that passed by, her gaze was broken by just one, approaching in the distance. She'd never forgotten her walk, slow but deliberate. The same stride Thuy had tried to match since the day they met, in an attempt to see Bian again, if only in herself. To see behind the locked door. To see the one who held her secrets.

Studio Girls

Amy Honeywell

ACT ONE.
SCENE ONE.

A studio flat in South East London. The flat is cramped but warmly lit by lamps. It's evening. Centre stage is a green sofa with small tables on either side. An old-fashioned dial telephone sits on the left table. Up-stage left is an unmade double bed, books are stacked neatly on the floor by one side while on the other there is a pink vibrator sticking out from under the bed. Stage right there is a clawfoot bathtub and a toilet. An empty door frame marks the entrance to the bathroom. The room is generally cluttered and untidy with clothes and old mugs strewn around the place. On the sofa sits BEV, the phone tucked between her ear and her shoulder while she lights a cigarette.

BEV:…And then she asked me what my favourite colour is…I know what a curveball, I don't think I even have one. Anyway, it threw me off and all I could think to say was 'my mum likes red.' Honestly Mum, it was horrendous, I don't think I've ever been on a worse date. Nope, couldn't bring myself to kiss her after that—I shook her hand and practically sprinted to the tube, I was so frantic I got on the wrong way and ended up in Brixton.

BEV: knocks the ash off her cigarette into an ashtray on the arm of the sofa. She shuffles around, pulling her feet up on the sofa. She makes phone sounds: mmm, yeah…true…well.
I don't know, I'm trying. I don't really have much to say about myself.

BEV: looks down and sniffs, the cigarette burning between her fingers forgotten. No Mum, I'm fine. I'm not crying. Don't be silly. BEV wipes her eyes on the sleeve of her sweatshirt. Look Mum, I have to go. Ryan'll be home any minute and she's bringing cake and tequila.
(beat)
Thanks Mum, I know, I miss you too. Next year will be our year, I promise. Okay, I love you. Bye Mum, bye.

BEV: hangs up the phone and stubs out her cigarette. She swings her feet to the floor, elbows on knees, she puts her head in her hands, her gaze sitting just above the audience. She zones out. After a couple of seconds there's the sound of banging and keys scraping in a lock. We hear RYAN before we see her. RYAN enters stage left wrapped up and carrying shopping bags.

RYAN: I'm going to dislocate my shoulder on that door one day.

RYAN: dumps the bags on the floor, shrugs off her coat and throws it on the unmade bed, quickly followed by her hat and scarf. She's cheery and bright, happy to be home. Happy birthday, Bev.

BEV: Thanks Ry.

RYAN: I got us profiteroles and some strawberries from the stall by the tube. They look a bit squashed for six quid, but the man was so friendly, and he gave me this giant courgette for free.

BEV: It's a marrow.

RYAN: What?

BEV: A marrow.

RYAN: Huh.

BEV: When courgettes get that big they turn into marrows.

RYAN: Oh, weird.
                    (beat)
Did you talk to your Mum?

BEV: Yeah, just got off the phone with her now. She says 'hi'.

RYAN: I can't believe I missed her again. She's such a crack-er, it's a shame she can't join us tonight. I haven't seen her since we got kicked out of Electric Ballroom.

BEV: I know, but she has this thing and she feels bad, but she said she's sending a present.

RYAN: ...I know, I know—we'll do a shot for her, hey?
                    (beat)
How's your day been?
BEV: Pretty boring, I don't know why I thought taking the day

off work was a good idea—I just sat here smoking, watching Loose Women and waiting for Rachel to text me.

RYAN: grimaces and picks up the open packet of cigarettes, taking one out and lighting it.

RYAN: She still hasn't texted you?

BEV: No, I think she thought I was boring.

RYAN: No!

BEV: I mean, I couldn't tell her what my favourite colour was.

RYAN: That doesn't mean you're boring, you're the least boring person I know.

BEV: You have to say that because you live in my flat.

RYAN: That's true.
                    (beat)
You're actually really boring.
BEV: Really?

RYAN: No! Jesus Christ, she doesn't deserve you. What did she say her favourite colour was?

BEV: Purple.

RYAN: Purple? Gross, we didn't want her anyway, who likes purple?

BEV: I like purple…

RYAN: No, you like pussy. You haven't been laid in so long your brain is turning to soup and you think you like purple. Next thing you'll be telling me you bought brown bread.

BEV: I bought brown bread.

RYAN: Oh my God, this is dire.

RYAN: takes a bottle of tequila from one of the shopping bags and picks up two used mugs from the floor. She sniffs one and proceeds to pour large glugs of tequila into each. She holds out a mug to BEV. BEV takes the mug. RYAN raises her own mug above her head. Stand up!

BEV: heaves up from the sofa. RYAN and BEV stand centre down-stage.To being 29, to being boring, to having sex again before hitting 30. BEV laughs. They drink. And to not going on dates with people who ask what your favourite fucking colour is. How old was she, 12?

(beat)

BEV: …21.

RYAN: Crikey Bev, you're really desperate.

BEV: I'm not desperate.

BEV: sits down and puts her head in her hands again, this time looking at the floor. She sighs. RYAN sits next to her. The sofa is cramped. RYAN rubs BEV's back gently then pulls her against her chest. RYAN wraps her arms around BEV in a close embrace.
I'm lonely. I don't really know what I'm doing…

RYAN: How can you be lonely? You've got me, you've got your mum, you've got…

BEV: says through a sob.

BEV: A birthday marrow.

RYAN: A birthday marrow!

RYAN: picks the marrow up from among the shopping bags on the floor. It's enormous. What do we do with it?

BLACKOUT.
END OF SCENE.
ACT ONE.
SCENE TWO.

A studio flat in South East London. It's dark, unlit. We hear crashing from offstage, keys scraping, laughing, banging. BEV and RYAN enter stage left. They're stumbling and talking loudly, clearly drunk. They turn the lamps on around the flat before sitting on the sofa. They are mid conversation.

BEV:—so I got us a couple of drinks and it was going great until this man showed up and I was like 'who are you?' and she was like 'oh this is Daniel, my boyfriend.' And I was like 'boyfriend?'

RYAN: She had a boyfriend the whole time?

BEV: The whole time.

RYAN: Do you think they were…

BEV: Absolutely, he came over, shook my hand and winked at me.

RYAN: Ew.

BEV: And then she started getting all up in my face and that's when you arrived.

RYAN: Perfect timing.

BEV: You saved me from whatever weird thing they had planned.

RYAN: It's funny though.

BEV: It's not! I really liked her.

RYAN: I know, but there are plenty of other women out there.

BEV: Where? I seem to only be able to find straight girls who want me to go down on them while their boyfriend watches.

RYAN: What about Rachel? She wasn't straight.

BEV: But she also hasn't text me since my birthday, it's been a week and a half.

RYAN: You're right, she's never coming back.

BEV: covers her face with her hands and groans.

BEV: I just want to be someone's priority.

RYAN: You're my priority, Bev.

BEV: But I shouldn't be, we're friends, we're not planning on spending the rest of our lives together.

RYAN: Why not? We've managed it so far—

BEV: Because that's not how things work, you'll meet a boy—

RYAN: Or a girl.

BEV: Or a girl, sorry. You'll meet someone and then you'll leave me, and I'll be here by myself smoking on the sofa and watching Jeremy Kyle until I die.

RYAN: That's not true and you know it.

BEV: Which bit?

RYAN: All of it! And anyway, you can come and live with me and my partner and be our live-in cool gay aunt who teaches the kids swear words and buys them cigarettes.
BEV: I don't want to be an extension of your life though, I want my own life.
                    (beat)
RYAN: You have your own life, Bev. It's a great life, a special one I'm grateful to share with you.
                    (beat)
BEV: Kiss me. RYAN is shocked

RYAN: What?

BEV: Kiss me.

RYAN: Bev, no.

BEV: But—
BEV: grabs for RYAN and pulls her on top of her so they are both lying on the sofa. RYAN is trying to prise herself away.

RYAN: Bev, come on, you're drunk, you don't really want to do this.

BEV: I just, I just—

RYAN: tries again to untangle herself from BEV, pushing her—

self up on her arms. Ryan, please. Everything calms, BEV's hands are on RYAN's waist. RYAN looks down at BEV and strokes her cheek.

RYAN: I love you, you know I do. RYAN leans down and gently kisses BEV on the mouth. But this isn't us.

BEV: But what about—

RYAN: That doesn't count.

BEV: Why?

RYAN: We were 15 and very high.
(beat)
It would just make things complicated. What would happen next?

BEV: …I don't know.

RYAN: We know each other too well and need each other too much for this to ever work that way.

BEV: I just don't remember what it feels like to be loved.

RYAN: looks at BEV softly and lowers herself down so her head is resting on BEV's shoulder. They wrap their arms around each other.

RYAN: This is what it feels like. I love you.

BEV: I love you, too.

BLACKOUT.
END OF SCENE.

Timeline of a Proper Domestic Life

Madeline Donnelly

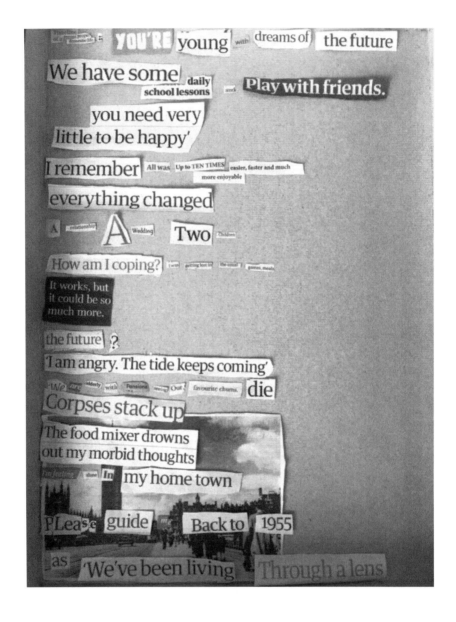

Timeline of a Proper Domestic Life
Madeline Donnelly

You're young with dreams of the future—we have some daily school lessons and play with friends—you need very little to be happy—I remember all was up to ten times easier, faster and much more enjoyable—everything changed—a relationship, a wedding, two children—how am I coping?—I was getting lost in the usual games, meals—it works, but it could be so much more—the future?—I am angry. the tide keeps coming—we are elderly with pensions seeing our favourite chums die—corpses stack up—the food mixer drowns out my morbid thoughts —I'm feeling alone in my home town—please guide me back to 1955 as we've been living through a lens—

He reads the words out loud, slowly, as if for emphasis, slides the poster across the desk to me. Words cut out from some newspaper and photocopied, my daughter's message to her mother, the mothers, to some extent the fathers, of all her friends, her teachers, the would-be parents, the would-be adults—in short, her message to the entire world. Words belonging to others, forming a message they never consented to. Frances' poster looks childish against the oak desk, amid the leather-bound books and framed portraits lining the walls of the Headmaster's office. Sometimes, I find it's easy to forget she's still a child, only just fifteen. I'm grateful for these reminders, the lopsided characters and torn edges.

'They're all over the school. Outside every classroom. About fifty tacked up on the ceiling of the chapel, though I'll be damned if I know how she managed that. The Vicar is very shaken. One over the face of the Messiah. An awful business. Almost heretical.'

It's hard to keep the smile off my face, the tears from trickling down my cheeks. I'm torn between multiple strange sensations of pride, jealousy, and hurt. The urge to laugh becomes almost uncontrollable when I picture Reverend Nurries's face on discovering the desecration of his sacred chapel. And yet - and yet - is this my life depicted in print? I'm not yet fifty, but am I, in my daughter's eyes, on a path leading to watching 'corpses stack up'? It works, but it could be so much more. Living through a lens.

Her dislike fills my lungs with water, every second I'm closer to drowning. But she does make me smile, make me so proud I could burst. Even when she tells me I don't love her, that all I care about is being 'picture-perfect'. I do, it isn't.

It's several moments before I can trust myself to speak. 'And how do you know it was Frances?' I enquire. If you didn't know my daughter, you'd believe the cuttings were an attempt to hide her identity. Instead, I suspect the cuttings are part of the message itself, a way to scream: IT'S WHAT WE'RE ALL THINKING. A counter to je ne regrette rien…you all know we regret everything.

'We asked her,' he tells me.

'You…asked her. And she admitted it?'

The Headmaster's moustache twitches. 'She did.' Picking up a note from his paper tray, 'She quoted George Orwell—I wrote it down, it was neatly done,

I thought you might like to see it…it's from Orwell's introduction to Animal Farm. A book I read a long time ago… didn't recognize it immediately…'

Once again, I feel an urge to smile, but reign it in. I read aloud, 'If liberty means anything at all it means the right to tell people what they do not want to hear.'

'Animal Farm is not on the school syllabus.'

'Frances reads a lot at home, she…' I stop when I see the Headmaster's face.

'Then she asked me if I was a Thatcherite.'

Frances… she likes to shock, when she knows the answer, she likes to put on a display. Another hidden smile.

The poster sits silent between us, a catalyst for whatever must come next. He tells me, 'There have been prior incidents which directed our investigations. They've been… well,' he shrugs his shoulders, as if easing the muscles of his conscience, 'emotionally disturbing. Lyrics scratched onto desks; refusing to do work; tantrums; matron tells me of reports that she screams in her sleep… that is, we have to think of the other girls. We're a respected establishment in this community, Mrs Lyle. But people have been talking. The Board— '

I can feel my cheeks flushing. God forbid that people should talk. And yet —God forbid it. The PTA will adore my family's disgrace. I can picture them smiling, offering their sympathies.

'Of Governors?' I finish weakly.

'Quite so. Mrs Lyle… I'm afraid this is one step too far.'

'Too… you don't mean…'

'I regret that we can no longer accommodate your daughter in our school. You can take her home with you tonight.' I stare at him. The red light reflected from the stained glass on the south wall frames his outline, veils his face, as if I were meeting with Satan himself. Or simply a man who doesn't want to act. To help, to protect. There's a long pause. Outside, I can hear well-kept voices strolling on well-kept lawns. I wonder if my daughter is among them, not knowing she's about to be banished from this place forever. 'Mrs Lyle,' the Headmaster says in somewhat of a softer tone, 'we do understand, you know. It isn't always the parents' fault… there are difficult children in many underserving families…'

Later, the door of the Headmaster's office closes sharply behind me. I'm shaking, my mind only now beginning to emerge from a strange sort of blackness, where I hardly knew what I was saying.

Did I beg? Scream? Say nothing at all?

I hope I said something. I hope I fought for her. Frances spends half her life fighting, so why shouldn't I just this once? I've failed, at any rate. I can picture Frances' triumphant expression collapsing to that of anger and disappointment, because of me. How strange that I should be so scared of disappointing her, when it's supposed to be the other way around. She has never seemed in the least wary of disappointing me.

In May 1979, Frances turned thirteen. In November, when Pink Floyd released Another Brick in the Wall, I was bombarded with complaints that my daughter had been climbing lamp posts outside the local primary and secondary schools, shouting at the top of her lungs: 'Hey, teachers, leave them kids alone.' Nothing I could say would stop her. Time did in the end, the changing of the seasons, a bout of the flu at the Maria of Bethany School for Girls, of which she'd been a pupil.

The school secretary, a neatly dressed woman of thirty-or-so years, is gazing at me like she can't quite believe what she's seeing. My hand automatically flies to my hair, scared that a strand has fallen askew. But everything is in place. Did I fight, then? There's a feeling, somewhere in my chest, like a bird pecking holes at my insides, ink dripping from the puncture wounds. Is it pride? In my left hand I'm clutching Frances' poster, a compilation of printed patches torn from my daughter's heart.

That night I'm lying in bed, reading. My husband is fast asleep beside me.

Timeline of a proper domestic life:

How am I coping? How am I coping?

1955, I was thirteen. Guide me back to... I remember a childhood steeped in fantasy, in wonder, in dreaming of dreams of a future that was going to be all that. I don't know when it all seemed to change, but my visions of the future suddenly seem lost in an irretrievable past. And in my heart there's a suspicion that life should feel like water droplets burning as they slam against pupils and veins, fingernails ripping open blood-vessels, the smashing of a skull on a cliff-face. Not like a thing that's waiting to feel, waiting to experience, a veil, dainty gloves slipping around my skin, my eyes, my tongue, silk coating my bloodstream. Not to feel like years have been spent waiting for THE BIG SOMETHING to occur. There are the big things, but they aren't, they haven't... not yet.

If the film would just break, if someone would just press pause for little while then life would come rushing in, like air, like rich blood, sapphire water. Life would fill up my senses. Life would taste, smell, feel, sound like ecstasy, a voice screaming into an empty moor at dawn. Years ago now I had a dream that rather than go back, I turned my eyes to the sun. As my corneas melted, I felt some peace. Living through a lens.

How am I coping?

I can hear Frances, alone in her bedroom, packing away her things. She's angry to be home, barely speaking two words to me at dinner, giving only one word an-swers to her father. Though, this afternoon in the school courtyard, she did pale when she saw her poster in my hand. And for the tiniest moment I thought she might be about to say sorry. I know my lips were forming the word.

With thanks to—

The Editing Team:
Emma Seager—Editor in Chief
Lucy May —assisting Editor in Chief
Jack Oxford—assisting Editor in Chief

Saskia Reynolds
Chiara Picchi
Polly Halladay
Lilly Boag
Flo Pearce-Higginson
Rebekah Jane Philipson
Beth Townsend
Beatrice Prutton
Lucy Pilgrim
Amelia Cox
Prerana Kumar
Elitsa Piriankov
Jure Sušnik
Frank Carver
Hamilton Brown
Alix Green
Lucy Cundill
Florence Strang Boon
Emma Liggins
Evie Pledger
Erin Ketteridge
Ryan Lenney

The Egg Box Committee:
Emma Seager—President
Dylan Davies—Vice president & Union Council Rep
Georgia Greetham—Events Officer and Workshop & Social Coordinator
Daisy Church—Social Secretary
Oliver Jay Shrouder—Treasurer and Health & Safety Officer
Oliver Hancock—Equality & Diversity Officer
Jack Oxford—Secretary
Kate Oskirko—First Year Representative

Under & Over

First published by Egg Box Publishing in 2021
Part of UEA Publishing Project Ltd
International ©2021 retained by individual authors
A CIO record of this book is available from the
British Library

Under & Over is typeset in Adobe Garamond Pro
Cover design and type setting by Anna Brewster
Printed and bound in the UK by Imprint Digital
Distributed by NBN International

ISBN: 978-1-913861-12-4

Eggbox Instagram:
@theeggbox

UNDER
&OVER

UEA UNDERGRADUATE
ANTHOLOGY 2020-2021